BE A GOOD BOY JOHNNY

John Tilsley

Ringpull • *Manchester*

First published in Great Britain in 1995 by Ringpull
an imprint of Fourth Estate Limited
6 Salem Road
London W2 4BU

Copyright © John Tilsley 1995

The right of John Tilsley to be identified as the author
of this work has been asserted by him in accordance
with the Copyright, Designs and Patents Act 1988.

City of New Orleans by Arlo Guthrie © Warner Brothers.
Reprinted by permission.

A CIP catalogue record for this book is available
from the British Library

ISBN 1-898051-30-5

Interior Design by Sandra Green
Typeset in 10/15 Caxton Book by
Palimpsest Book Production Limited,
Polmont, Stirlingshire
Printed in England by Clays Limited, St Ives plc

FOR WAYNE AND THE BOYS ON THE WALL

GO EASY FELLAS

CONTENTS

MURDER ONE 1

It was August. The sun was dipping slowly behind the run-down motels and pick-up trucks. Across the way on a vacant lot a flea-bitten dog lays claim to a discarded chilli dog, raising dust as he paws his new-found take-away. I look down and check the Rolex. It's twenty after six, no hurry. It is Friday and early hours for this crazy town. Cracking open two cans of beer I hand one to Wayne then push the remains of the six-pack into the shade behind me.

The ice-cold Coors gives a bite to my parched throat. It sure feels good. Dragging the T-shirt across the crease of my belly I mop the sweat then pat the dust from my Levis. A warm desert breeze blows in from the west, caressing and cooling my upper body. It's small talk. I enjoy the old-timer's tales. Wayne's been in these parts some fifteen years; he is a rum old bastard and a tale he can tell.

In twenty minutes our group has grown to eight, all sitting on the motel wall. Most nights Wayne and I enjoy a few beers, watching the sun set. Tonight is a little different. We have company on the low wall that skirts the southern face of our motel. Some times we get the odd street person bumming a beer. But tonight all sat on the wall are local to the area, all resident to some low-down motel room. Always it seems when the wall becomes inter-racial there appears a pecking order – the two niggers are sat on the flank.

The second beer is going down a treat. Cans are popping and the shit is getting worse: the younger amongst us shooting bullshit, everyone an expert on sex, drugs and rock 'n' roll. I listen to the loose talk, keeping my conversation with Wayne. I'm the odd ball on this wall, a Brit. I have been around more than most, so I know a few of the rules, and one of them is being a good listener. Wayne rocks his empty can from side to side. I reach behind and produce a new beer. He knows this method of asking gets on my tits but he never makes any effort to amend. Still, Wayne gets his beer plus a five dollar bill. He slopes off in the direction of the Seven-Eleven to purchase a fresh six-pack.

The sun is casting long shadows across the wide roads and sidewalks. *Bang!* My eyes focus swiftly. It's an old Chevy pick-up, back-firing down Carson Street. White Texan registration plates. Hell, he will be lucky to make the State line.

With Wayne now somewhere between here and Timbuktu, my immediate neighbour is a middle-aged Hispanic, who, at his request, remains nameless to us. He tells the same story all the time and he's telling it once again, and once again nobody is listening. Wife and two kids back in Fresno, two cars in the garage and a pick-up out front. One sad day no-name takes a crack smoke. That's it, within two months the whole fucking kaboosh has gone up in smoke. He drops his head. He should instead take a long hard look at the niggers. It is their trade that helped him on to this low, low wall.

Chilli dog throws me a detached glance. All ribs and dick, Chilli and Wayne could make a good street story. He takes a piss then slopes off in search of better company.

At first I don't hear the steady tap of high heel shoes. I'm watching the pick-up making a right on to Seventh. Tap tap. My head turns in the direction of that steady tap. Now I'm looking at the owner, a tall slim Anglo-blonde, great legs and a great pair of tits.

"May I join you boys? Sure need to rest my feet awhile."

She is offered a beer before her arse hits the wall. She sits on the other flank from me, parked with the niggers. I get preoccupied rolling a Samson and making plans for the evening. Where the fuck is Wayne?

I have my ears well open to the cross-talk between the blacks and the blonde. The blacks deal crack from apartments one block east on Fremont. It makes me nervous mixing it with these dope heads. I am eighteen months adrift on Uncle Sam's visitors' visa and if the Drugs Enforcement Agency is staking these boys, I'm in a world of shit. There seems to be no direct connection between Angel and the blacks. Interesting, because these blacks know every face and where it comes from on these streets. I am also sure they would have smelled a rat if she was a cop working undercover. Another thing. She is too articulate. She don't belong to these mean streets. This is downtown Las Vegas, tough streets and one can be in that world of shit in a heartbeat.

Wayne's making his way home, wobbling along Carson, the weight of the six-pack somehow pulling him to one side of the sidewalk then releasing him back again. He has been on the piss all day and his old liver just ain't making it. He plops on the wall with a thud but the beer is gently laid to rest in the shade.

"You're a good old boy, you know that John?"

Wayne leans forward to give the blonde the once over; Wayne is saved from falling on his face by another member of our group, Steve. Rocking backwards, Wayne nudges me and puckers his lips.

"You wouldn't? Would you John?"

Wayne is struggling now, his speech is slurred and he is in a position of making a serious prat of himself.

"Don't worry about the beer Wayne. Take a couple of cans for the morning."

He gets the message and moseys off into the cool of the motel.

The original eight has thinned down to three. The blacks have melted into the half-light to ply their trade. The blonde moves into the space vacated by Wayne, an expensive fragrance stimulates the void.

"English?"

"Yeah."

"Here on vacation?"

"No, I work down on Main."

"What kind of work?"

"Does it matter? What's your name?"

"Angel, and yours?"

Give me a break, who gives names like this? Yeah, once upon a time when she was swinging off her mother's tit. But now forty if she's a day, been around the block a few times and carrying plenty of mileage. Still . . . those tits!

"My name's John. Pleased to meet you Angel. Do you belong to these parts?"

"No John, I'm from Reno. Here visiting friends and kicking back. I fly back on Sunday."

We talk some. I'm on my last can and in desperate need of a shower and a change of underwear, so if this conversation ain't going anywhere I'm ready to split.

"This your motel John?"

I reach into my pocket as she pulls a soft pack.

"Sure is. It ain't the Queens', but it's all I need at the moment. Fancy stepping out tomorrow night Angel? Meal, a few beers maybe?"

The flame from my Zippo dances light and shadow across her face. The Marlboro glows as she inhales deeply. A few seconds pass. She must have been some looker in her day. Even now, the lines that etch her eyes and mouth give added strength to her maturity.

"OK John, tomorrow night we'll go down the Strip, if that's alright with you. A dealer owes me alimony."

"Which casino?"

"Tropicana. I'll make a call later to make sure what shift he is working. Make it eight o'clock. Any change I'll call by the motel tomorrow daytime and leave a message."

"Eight tomorrow then. Give me a knock on room 105. You take care Angel."

She is up on her feet and striding out towards Fremont. That long confident catwalk stride. Yeah, she sure got style. This could be kinda interesting.

I collect up the empty cans and deposit them in the black bin liner provided by Wayne, his perks. He weighs them in every couple of weeks to buy a few beers. He ain't got a pot to piss in so he's ever grateful. Wayne gets his doss for nothing on account of him being the resident maid. He's sixty if he's a day with one lone tooth roaming around his mouth, bald as a badger with a face torn with booze. It says a lot about the opulence of this doss. But Wayne's a straight shooter. I stand him the beers on account of him looking after my room when I'm away from the motel.

Stepping inside I place the bin liner outside Wayne's door, the closest to the entrance. The motel stinks of old piss. The smell is buried in the walls. All the disinfectant they shake about ain't going to remove that. The front door has been missing for days. Where it went is a mystery to inmates and the manager. Anyway, this act of vandalism is causing lots of problems. Dopers shoot their flesh along the corridor in the early hours, then collapse in doorways to be tripped over or, in my case, kicked at first light. These encounters are rare, because before the morning's light can penetrate the full length of the corridor, they are dragged away by kindly persons unknown and placed besides the dumpster at the rear of the motel.

This place ain't seen a lick of paint since they threw it up, and the carpets must have seen the coming of the Mormons; threadbare isn't the word. There seems to be more concrete showing than carpet. Still, I ain't moaning. The rent comes cheap at seventy-five a week. It's

just a place to keep clean and rest my head.
This motel has been my home since I arrived
in Vegas from New Mexico four months ago.
The motel's got a tough reputation. It's called
the *M1 RESIDENTIAL MOTEL*. On the streets
M1 has been explained to me as Murder One. A
right mixture of tenants she holds at the moment:
crack dealers work out of 112, several hookers
work out of rooms by the rear exit door. The
rest are mainly old men, whose main vocation
is stumbling about, coughing and farting, the
welfare check paying the room. Some bastard
has also stolen the rear exit door, possibly the
crack dealers, so we have constant foot traffic
in the hallway all through the night. It is also to
the advantage of the hookers, who knock on all
the inmates' doors, old and young alike, every
Thursday night. An old bunch of dogs they are
too, but then they blend in with the decor.

The double bed takes up most of the floor
area. A bedside locker and open-plan wardrobe,
and a broom handle wedged in the wall recess,
makes up room 105. There is a television but it
don't work. Every Friday when I pay the rent it's
going to get fixed. It never does.

The beer, drunk empty stomach, is taking
its toll. I'm knackered. It's been a long hot day.
Opening the bedside locker drawer I pick up the
.38 snub nose revolver. The uncertain weight,
heavy for its compact size, and the cold and blue

steel feel reassuring. Click, the cylinder rests in my left palm, the brass bases of the snub nose bullets exposed. All in order. I gently close the piece and rest it on top of the bedside locker. This weapon I know from experience is not too powerful, but in a twelve by twelve room and with this kind of ammunition I'm sure as hell gonna cause a shit storm!

The shower washes away the day's grime but I give the change of underwear a miss. Looking square into the mirror I scratch on the four day growth, fingers dance along a scar; they move high on the cheek-bone close to the ear then down above my right shoulder. Three years old and I still feel the Stanley blade. The hour hand sweeps through ten as I hit the lights.

My eyes open slowly, adjusting to the bright sunlight pouring through the thin curtains. My stomach feels like my throat's been cut so I'm quickly on my feet and taking a piss in the handbasin. That's one thing that is universal, the height of handwash basins. The .38 is slid into the drawer, quick swill, brush of the teeth and I'm out of the door. Wayne's bin-liner is missing. It's seven-thirty, perhaps he is up, or has some disgruntled punter nicked them on the way out. Tough shit Wayne!

Outside the sidewalk is cool and the sky is an artist's blue. The sun is low but its strength is beginning to tell. The start of another long hot day.

Crossing Fremont I take the corner entrance into the El Cortez, a popular downtown casino and hotel. On opening the door the freshness of the early desert air is replaced by the smell of mild decay, bad breath, whatever. In seconds I'm acclimatised and threading my way through the rattle of slot machines, tables playing with croupiers still wide-eyed, and sharp, neon cowboys, eyes like piss holes in the snow, throwing in their last few dollars. Narrow-eyed pit bosses, their stares shifting from dealer to dealer, move from table to table. Eight o'clock western time and the place is buzzing. It's like this now and it's like this twenty-four hours a day, every day.

The one dollar twenty cent best-deal-breakfast line is a little quieter than usual, maybe ten or twelve people and I join the queue. In front of me two middle-aged Spanish women are gabbling away. Lucky in bed or lucky on the tables? I don't know. I understand a little Spanish, but these women are too quick. The pale-faced waitress walks the line towards me.

"Excuse me honey, there's a gentleman wants you to join him for breakfast."

Gentleman! I don't know any gentlemen. I follow her gaze. It's Tony, sat alone at a two person booth. Tony belongs to the same motel. He arrived two weeks ago from Texas, carrying four grand, plenty of gold and ambition. He's left a wife and four kids back home to come here and strike it rich. Join the queue Tony, you ain't going to make it. I make across to Tony, six booths in from the waitress station. I notice his fingers ain't showing the gold rings. Tony's in the shit!

"Take a seat John, how ya doin'?"

"Pretty good, you?"

He don't look too good. He's spent the last twelve hours in smarter company. Tony is not going to make the poker hall of fame down at Binnions Horse Shoe Hotel. He shakes his head.

"No good. Fuck, I had it all going at two this morning, but shit, I'm in the hole for seven hundred."

I really don't want to listen, but what can I do trapped in a two seater booth.

I order the dollar twenty cent breakfast special from the none too masculine waiter. He pours black coffee then minces off.

"Do you think you could do me a favour John?"

"Ask me Tony."

"I got me a pinkie ring in hock on Third. It's got to be worth seven hundred bucks 'cause the hock stood me one eighty on it. You know it's got to be three times the value, right?"

I do know, and he knows I know. I make my money buying up fine jewellery from luckless gamblers like Tony. I airmail it back to a dealer in

London who then mails back cash return-of-post. It's a good earner, a very good earner. Punters know me in the downtown area but it has to be kept low key. Like most other things in Las Vegas, apart from gambling, it's illegal. It can also be a little dangerous. Most of the business is executed in motel rooms and on a cash basis so I have got to be thinking on my feet always. It's all down to street psychology and that split second reading of strangers' faces.

"Tell you what I'll do Tony. We'll go down Third at midday. If, and only if, I like the look of the ring, I'll cash it out. If you ain't got the money to me in one week's time, the ring is mine. OK?"

"Listen John, I got a settlement due to me from Houston. It will be here in one week no problem. Thanks a lot buddy."

"Hey! No problem my end, so long as we understand the rules. OK?"

Tony rises to leave, spreading the palms of his hands wide, like we just made some bonding. Tony's an arsehole so I'm happy to see the back of him. Ten minutes later I'm on my last fork of hashbrowns and any more coffee I'll be pissing it through all day long.

Tony's on time. Right he is. He needs this deal more than me. Each day the pinkie lays in the hock, it's burning him five bucks on top of the one eighty. We walk the four blocks to Third, keeping in the shadows to shield the sun. It's hot as hell. Twenty minutes later I have the ring in my pocket. It looks a good deal, but I can check that out later. Outside the hock Tony counts the bills while I make excuses: I have a lunch date. Tony enters the nearest Casino while I make for Fremont and Seventh.

Sam is busy, hunched over the long glass-counter. My face, pressed up close to the door's glazing, cuts off some daylight into the shop. Sam lifts himself upright, hands rubbing the small of his back. His back arched, the big old .44 revolver stands proud in the front of his waistband. Tucked deep, the dark handle clashes with the white of his shirt. Sam reaches forward then motions me to push the door as the buzzer sounds.

"How ya doin' John? What you got for me today?"

"A pinky, Sam."

"What you pay?"

"One eight five. Any good?" Sam reaches into his shirt pocket. The eye-piece moves slowly over the ring.

"Give me a minute. Gonna sell me that watch?"

The ring is getting the third degree. Sam's an alright guy. He don't need to value the ring, but I put business his way. The last package I mailed back to London, Sam had a twenty per cent interest. When I leave the city, Sam can use my London contact.

"Mens five cluster diamond, eighteen carat, slight flaw in one stone. You got yourself a good buy there. London will love it, believe me."

"Thanks Sam. Hey! I'm about ready to post again. You have anything?"

"Not this time John. You be lucky now." I hang the shade as I head for my safe deposit on Main.

Back out on the sidewalk and torching a tailor-made, I spot Jimmy, propping up a US Mail bin on the corner of Lewis. He's looking along Lewis making out he didn't see me enter the deposit. I play his game and walk in the opposite direction. I feel his eyes following me. Wait for it!

"Hey John! Fancy that would you! What you doin' here this time a day?" He is panting after his effort to get up to me.

"You seen me all along, didn't you John?" It looks like it is gonna be one of those days!

Down Main we walk.

"I seen you Jimmy, you're hangin' in like a bad smell. I thought maybe you'd give up on this town?"

He gets closer, I edge away. He keeps coming.

"I got something lined up. But Jesus, I'm sleepin' most nights down at the Hall. I got niggers an' bugs crawlin' all over me man! I got to get out."

"You look an' smell like shit. You need to right away. You hear me?"

"That's it man! Could you do me forty-five John? Catch me a Greyhound to San Francisco. What you say buddy?"

"Fuck me Jimmy! You're a pain in the arse, you know that? Walk with me on to Fremont, I'll buy you a coffee."

Jimmy goes back before Vegas, right back to a salad bar in Flagstaff, Arizona. Minding my business and forcing a five buck all you can eat down my neck, Jimmy joins me at the table, and if I remember right, there were plenty of tables spare. Early thirties, blond hair and blue eyes, six tall and lean. The all American boy out of Brooklyn, Jimmy opens up with wise guy spiel. I figure that in his eyes anybody this far south is registered brain dead. He might have had me down for brain dead, but I had something on the parking lot he needed real bad: wheels, four of them.

I'm forcing the lettuce while he's forcing some bullshit story about shunting a rod through his block. This boy don't even own a car key, in fact no keys. He looks one suitcase and trouble, but it's half a day's ride into Vegas and I reckon I can stand about that.

"A ride I'm after buddy an' that's all." Well, a ride he got but what a pain in the tail. A real live bullshit artist. What he ain't going to do in Vegas! If Bugsy Seagal had met with him forty years back, Bugsy would have shot straight through to Utah. No kidding! This guy is going to light up the skies and I need this like a racoon needs a hat stand.

We hit town and room together in a place little better than the M1. I don't know the M1 then, but we're just one block west. He stands his half on the one week's rent then takes off blind into the downtown casinos. He says he has people to see in those casinos and they will find him work. Jimmy is full of shit but I'll give him one week. I have my doubts about Jimmy, but he's paid his half with the rent and if he don't come good in that time I'll split and go it alone. Two hours later I'm resting on the single and thinking nothing in particular when Jimmy returns with a face as long as a gas man's mack. It's a story I'm going to hear so many times. The problem here is, I'm gonna hear it from the person who is supposed to be sharing the rent. He has done his dough, right down to the last nickel. So now I have a room-mate who is destitute. OK, he has his room for one week, but how's he gonna feed himself? He smokes like a fucking chimney. Where's he going to get his fags? I don't believe it!

So, the big shot has shot his bolt. I won't see him starve or reduced to nicotine fits, but it's burgers and roll-ups and I put it gently like: if he ain't got work and wages by the week's end, he's in the shit and can go fuck himself. The rest of the week, Jimmy spends sleeping and watching the television, and that's another thing – it must be at melt down, belching all kinds of shit into the room twenty-four hours a day.

On the rare occasion he ventures out, he's eating giant dollar-a-pop hot dogs down at Lady Luck. Knowing he hasn't a cat's chance of finding work I make a reservation down at the M1. Jimmy looks at me with disbelief when we split. Now, there's another rule: never carry a passenger. Unless of course it weighs in under one hundred and twenty pounds and has a twat between its legs. It always turns sour.

Only last week, Jimmy catches me in the Golden Spike. He's in real bad shape. He has sold so much blood down at the donor centre that he's been awarded a gold medal. He queues every morning outside the labour office on Carson. Five-thirty, freezing his luckless bollocks off in the hope of, after administration stoppages, a fifteen dollar pay day. The world ain't holding out any hope for Jimmy, 'cept me. He bummed a ten spot only last week and asked, or should I say begged, if he could use my room to shower down. That's where I drew the line. Once inside I would have had the devil's own job getting rid of him.

His clothing is dirty and his shoulders bent, a failed street apprentice. Coffee, a hot dog and forty-five bucks later (yes, he got his dough, mixing it with sad stories and how he's going to make it all up to me one day), he shuffles off in the direction of the bus terminal. Should

18

I follow? What's the use. I somehow see him trying his luck before he hits the terminal. Just one more shot. Another thing, Jimmy don't have that wiseguy walk and talk anymore.

MIDNIGHT ON FREMONT 2

Seven forty-five and I'm shit, shaved and shampoo'd. Legs swinging off the edge of the bed replacing the flint in the Zippo. Tap . . . tap.

Angel looks a treat. Red high heels, tight Levis, tighter sweatshirt and masculine check sports coat.

"Hi John."

"Step inside Angel. You're a little early."

She drops her heavy shoulder bag on to the bed then leans against the wall. I refuse the offered cigarette and check the window is secure. Let's go.

"How we gonna do this John? Cab or bus?"

"Fuck the bus Angel. Saturday night, it will be bumper to bumper on the Strip. We'll catch a cab outside the Four Queens."

"OK John. My ex is dealing until ten. We got plenty of time."

The cab heads west off Fremont on to the freeway that skirts the city, then swings south to run parallel, overlooking the Strip. The Tropicana is at the extreme opposite end of the Strip to downtown, some four miles. This is the one major casino I have never been in, but once inside it will look and sound like the rest, tacky and noisy. The cabbie breaks every known driving rule in the book so by the time we hit the casino ramp I am in need of a drink. I lead in and head for the nearest bar.

"What's your poison Angel?" No reply. "Two Buds pal. Hey, make 'em bottles."

Angel grabs her bottle then heads off in the direction of the gaming tables. I settle on to the barstool and take a look around me. This place is pretty plush. I would say one of the better of the old establishment.

"Hi John."

"Christ! That was quick Angel. All done?"

"No, he can't get off the table for another ten minutes. I have to meet him in the dealers' room." She shrugs her shoulders.

She lights a cigarette. Her hand is shaky and the colour is drained from her face. She notes my concern and shrugs her shoulders again.

"It's been a long time. He usually mails it. I'm just a little nervous that is all."

"You did call him, didn't you? He is expecting you? Yes?"

"I'll be alright. Get me a stiff one will you honey, JD on the rocks." Without a word she grabs her glass, about turns and takes off on walkabouts. I hope she comes back with a smile; If not she can take a walk, there is plenty of loose pussy in this town.

A casual but smartly dressed guy takes the

corner stool. Bracelet and turquoise *corbata*. He waves a fifty at the bartender and my thoughts drift back to Jimmy. I lightly stroke the stainless watch strap, making double sure it's snapped tight. The Tonys and Jimmys fall fast in a city like this, farther then perhaps any city. I look over to the stool, the dude has gone. Fifteen minutes later she's back.

"Sorry John, we had to go to his car. Let me get these. I sure as hell need a drink."

She taps both jeans' pockets, reaches into them and brings together two rolls of bills. In the half light I don't catch the dollar denomination size. The bills are quickly rolled together and stuffed into one pocket. Some alimony!

She necks the JD and is looking restless.

"Let's go John."

Outside on the forecourt we quickly flag a cab. The driver eases the car on the freeway to take us back downtown. I feel relaxed and so is Angel. She takes my hand then gently kisses me on the cheek. Good. Looking down on the Strip below, the neon from hundreds of casinos and restaurants lights up the black desert sky. Like a rainbow arching the city. A cool breeze blows in the half-opened window. It feels good. I can see the boys back home, staggering out of some Tetley House, a belly full of hot piss, making towards the nearest bookies to back the last three losers at Haydock Park before arriving home to a grand bollocking having gambled and pissed the household money up the wall.

"Drop us on Fremont pal."

"I gotta fare to pick up at the Golden Nugget. That OK?"

Angel pays the fare and orders the drinks at the Nugget bar. Things are looking up. I'm still tipping beer but Angel's throwing back Jack Daniels like it's going out of fashion. For a fleeting second I note Angel make eye contact with someone. I don't see the person. He or she has melted into the mass of gamblers at the back of the room. She starts to act edgy. The shoulder bag that only two hours ago was stuck to her like glue, is left on the bar stool as Angel takes off in the direction of the eye contact. Yeah! one hour ago that black bag was stuck to her like shit to a blanket. Funny thing as well, the bag looks a lot lighter.

Bastard! Have I been stitched up? Was this a dope run? It couldn't be, could it? The old brains going into overdrive – the bag had to be full of dope. Whoever the buyer, she must be now divvying the money in the shitter. Nice one Johnny boy, who the fucking else is watching the show? Whatever, it's too late now. If damage has been done, it's been done. Shall I follow her to the rest room? No, I'll play the rest of the evening out and see how the cards are dealt.

Over the next three hours we booze and play the slots down Fremont. The Four Queens, Horse

Shoe, Fitzgeralds and then the El Cortez. The place smells better than it did this morning. Is it me or the change of clientele? It's certainly not the booze; I have been taking it steady, letting Angel neck the 'straight ups'. Man, can she drink. The eyes are beginning to get shot but she still has steady legs.

"It's getting late Angel. What do you want to do?"

Somehow during the evening the expected meal never made it. I ain't in the mood now anyway. It's murder to get seating this time of night, with casinos banging out cheap meals to draw in the punters. It seems Vegas starves itself all day long to eat this cheap food, most of it rubbish.

"What you want to do John?"

"We are only a block away from my place. Let's grab a pint of JD then settle in. What do you say?"

"Let's do it!"

We make our purchase on Las Vegas Boulevard, just one block away. It's only a short walk but at this time of the morning you got to be thinking on your feet – one reason I rarely touch hard liquor on the streets. The street people ain't too bad; they will hustle but at this early hour most of them will be off the street getting their heads down. Most are not Nevada residents and are very wary of the police. Any shit, the cops run them out to the County line. Some walk back.

The most dangerous are the dope heads,

spaced out, scouting for the odd stray who may
have got lucky at the tables. We walk, keeping
away from store doorways, staying on well-lit
sidewalks. When I'm on my own these problems
don't arise, it's all done without a thought. These
people know who to fuck with. If you look like you'll
return the shit, they won't hassle. With a woman in
tow it's different; you're looking out for two. I must
be getting old.

Back in room 105, the top spins off the
sour mash. Two shot glasses are produced and
we are ready to party. Two things are driving me
crazy. How much money is stashed in those jeans'
pockets? and those tits! Man, she ain't wearing
a bra but those babies are standing to attention.
The whisky tastes bitter sweet at the back of my
throat as I watch Angel prop up the pillows making
herself comfortable. She places the shot glass on
the bedside table and flicks a Marlboro from the
pack. I slide the Zippo across the bed; she snaps
it into action. Now she's looking at me.

"Where you from John? Stateside I mean?"

"I spent the first sixteen months in New
Mexico. The Land of Enchantment and all that."

"Yeah, I know it. Which part?" She is refilling
her glass.

"Santa Fe. Really got spoilt, some beautiful city."

"What made you leave?"

That's a long story and I ain't going into it

right now. I pour myself a large one. There are more important matters.

"You got to tell me Angel, are those tits real?"

"Sure are honey, real live silicone. You're looking at a cool six grand. Old money."

"Really?" I guess old money means twenty year back and the way she's moving into the upright position she's about ready to show me at least three grand's worth.

Her arms cross and the sweat shirt is peeled off. Man alive! This girl would never sink in the roughest sea.

"Feel this one John." I begin to explore. Poking and prodding like doctor dick, hoping somehow they will come to life. There is no life in these silicone globes. These are not a patch on your best mate's missus at your New Year's Eve grope, drooping like spaniels' ears but having that weight when lifted into the Happy New Year position.

No, I'm not getting off on these, not one bit! I can see this ain't going to be one of my better nights but now I've seen these it's the other item I'm interested in, the jeans' pocket.

The jeans are off and she's parading up and down the room. The scant briefs expose nothing, I've seen more hair on one of Bill the butcher's oven-ready chickens. It's a nightmare. If I would have known this at eight o'clock last night, I wouldn't have opened the fucking door! This is going to require all my professional tact.

"Any rubbers Angel?"

"No. I thought you would have a pack. Take a walk to the El Cortez. Machines in the rest room – you'll need quarters."

She's necking the whisky, pointing her glass towards the door.

"Go on."

"Fuck you! I ain't taking no walk this time of the morning."

"And fuck you too! You ain't getting none of this, baby!" It looks like I have negotiated a compromise.

The next hour flies by. She's pissed and I'm getting knackered and impatient. Her speech is slurred and time and time again I gently coax her from one tragedy or another. Like taking off into the dark night, naked and stupid. At long last she keels over on her side, shot and out for the count. I watch over her for ten minutes. She's snoring and snorting like an old pig. God help me, the things we have to go through! Her jeans lay crumpled against the bedside locker. She is out there in some other world. In my world I hear her snoring and as I edge my way along the bed towards the Levis, she lets out a loud fart. Jesus!

The roll of bills feels fat in my fist. Spreading them out on the end of the bed I separate the tens and twenties. The one dollar bills don't amount to much: thirty-five bucks. The bigger bills are getting interesting. A fifty appears now and then. Boy, I'm getting hard. One thousand dollar stacks – sixteen, seventeen. Seventeen thousand and fifty-five dollars and loose change. Some alimony. Yes! I've been taken for a right cunt. That wasn't smoke in the shoulder bag. It had to be coke or crack. Yeah, the heavy shoulder bag. The tensions before her meet with her ex. The quick exit from the casino. The dash for the rest room in the Nugget. God! How much dough was she packing before that meet in the Nugget?

The bills are rolled and stashed back deep into her Levi pocket. I light one of her cigarettes and lie down besides her. I have been used for this enterprise. The perfect escort. Englishman on vacation, wide-eyed and unassuming. Nice one Angel. My head is spinning. I reach for a shot glass, mine or hers, it don't matter. The glass don't make my lips. No, keep your cool. Did . . . did she say she would be back in two weeks time? I'll think clearer in the morning. The cigarette is stubbed and the light killed. Goodnight America.

I squint across at Angel. She looks like the angel of death this morning. Rays of the early morning sun are dancing across her profile. My head raises six inches then crashes back on to the pillow. How it aches! I rub my eyes and wait for them to focus. Angel stirs, groaning. She turns on to her side, her arm twisted behind her head. Long, slender fingers entwined in her fine blonde hair.

The kettle makes steam while I rinse the large mug and pop in the strongest tea bag I have managed to discover here in the States. The movements awaken Angel. She struggles on to her elbow. The sheet falls exposing those ample breasts.

"Make mine a coffee. Black, straight up."

"Sorry, tea is all we got."

"You English and your goddamn tea." Her flat white belly is now exposed.

All of a sudden Angel ain't looking too bad, or is it that my dick is doing all my thinking. Whatever, down there I feel the rush of blood.

I turn to face her and her eyes linger on my midriff. Those eyes tell me to move in closer. No problem. Straddling her face, both my hands clutch her golden hair, pulling her on to me.

"Light me a cigarette honey." The love juice shines on the side of her neck, patches that she missed when wiping with the edge of the flimsy curtain.

"What time's your flight?"

"Two p.m. Can you drive me? You have a pick-up, right?"

I nod my head. She is getting dressed now. Out of the corner of my eye I see her feel around the jeans' pocket. It does not seem a big deal. Is this small fry? Her face shows no emotions. There are no hesitations in her movements. She's a pro alright.

She dismisses my offer of tea as she splashes her face in the wash basin.

"Forget the tea John, I gotta run."

She dresses quickly. Cigarettes and lighter find her shoulder bag. Deft, deliberate movements, she's all business. I look on in silence then watch from the door as she strides down the corridor. As she passes Wayne's door, his head pops out, his eyes glued to her arse as she exits on to Carson. He turns in my direction, a great toothless smile. *Lucky bastard* reads all over his face. Yes Wayne, luckier than you might think old pal.

I close the door behind me, knackered. I think I'll inspect the back of my eyelids. Drawing the curtains tight I turn in. The slamming of a door in the corridor uneases me. I turn and try another position. I know the faces behind that door. Now I listen to their idle chatter. The dopers that occupy that room are one major headache. Morning, noon and night they deal in the open doorway, sometimes behind it. Whatever, there is always plenty of noise when transactions take place. Night-time is worst, their loudness echoes through the building. The old-timers who take up most of the space are either too worn out or old to object, so remain behind closed doors.

It was on my fourth night in 105. Apart from the occasional police helicopter clipping overhead, its spotlight searching for someone out there but in turn stealing my darkness, you could have heard a pin drop. Eyes closed, I hear the old boy next door emptying his lungs in the basin; he won't have insurance, so forty a day helps move the shit off his chest. Bang! Check Big Ben. One ten. Bang! Eyes pop open and my body stiffens. The banging is at my door. Shit! The banging comes with argument. I cannot grasp its meaning. The talk is hurried and excited. There must be at least five of them, quickly I jump floor space and flick the wall light, picking up the .38 before I lie back on the bed.

The noise about what they are going to do with me is getting worse. I should be shitting myself. The .38 lays by my side. Come on in boys, the hammer's back and the first one in is gonna get it. I got this lot figured full of wind and piss anyways, so, a little shaky after such an abrupt awakening, I'm steady and ready. Now I'm reading their story. It all centres around a television set, lent to the then occupier of my room two weeks ago. He lets in a prostitute (he must have got stoned on wacky baccy); she legs it with what money he has, plus the television. Now, these fuckers ain't got a clue what month they are in, never mind the day. They have been popping and sticking that long now the real world left them for dead years ago. As far as they are concerned, it's still the television man that's behind the door. That's me. I just wish I had a set that worked.

Kicks and thumps rain upon the door, but

are they really serious? Five men could push this
building over, so what's a badly-fitted door. I wait
and I watch the door vibrate. All of a sudden there
is deadly silence. Have the cops arrived? Their door
slams shut. Shit! The .38 is tucked into the locker
drawer as I move to the door and squint through
the spy hole. I don't see nothing but I feel any
second someone is going to come into view. Sure
enough, now I see him. A little guy, naked except
for a pair of once white baggy Y-Fronts. A box of
beer is clutched to his chest – he looks a sight.

"Hold it there!" booms a voice in the corridor.

"Go fuck yourself!" comes the reply. It ain't
the cops! Now I have both of them in my arc. The
pursuer wears a Seven-Eleven top and now the
penny has dropped.

Y-Fronts had been winged out of the room
opposite to fetch the beer, or was he was bringing
it along as a token of friendship for the dopeheads?
Nice words for such scumbags. Anyways, he
wouldn't look out of place wandering downtown
in nothing but a pair of underpants, would he?
The state of him, it's a wonder he wasn't picked
up by the dog patrol. Then into the Seven-
Eleven. Mildred, the night-shift assistant, must
have thrown a dicky fit. Y-fronts is definitely not
a full bag. He nicks the beer and now has the Seven-
Eleven night manager, Joe Montana, on his tail.
He's banging at the door. It's not going to open.

"Got yer bastard! I'm makin' an arrest. Hands agin the woll motherfucker."

Y-fronts is pleading. Banging like he's going to knock the door down. "Open this fuckin' door man! Let me in you no good bastards."

"I have a stun gun, an' if you don't surrender I'm goin . . ." Stun gun! Surrender! This guys been watching too many movies. My eye is now stuck to the spy hole. I see them both clearly. Y-fronts pitches the box at the manager, misses by miles and gets the dreaded prod from the stun gun. A screech and he falls out of sight. Man! This is better than the movies.

Mildred must have called the cops. Right away, sirens and blue light are flashing through my curtains. I run back and count three cars, there may be more around the corner. I lie back on the bed as cops pound the passageway. Political correctness don't come with the job; the thief is verbally abused, struck into, then bundled roughly outside. All in all a pretty good floor show. I only wish those opposite had opened their door and let him in. Perhaps then the cops would have kicked the shit out of them also. Still, they'll come another day. My eyes feel heavy. My position is comfortable. There'll be another . . .

"Hi John." Angel's on time for her ride to the airport. Her hold-all slides on to the centre of the bench seat. The cab is as hot as hell. We

have no air conditioning so the Chevy will ride hot
until we get some cool air blowing through the
open windows. The Chevy rumbles on to Carson,
the mighty engine block easing us up to Las Vegas
Boulevard. Left at the lights and straight down the
Strip to Desert Inn Road. Las Vegas in the light of
day is no different from any south-western city.
The glamour of Vegas is the night and the neon.
Right on to Paradise heading straight as an arrow
for McCarren International Airport. The traffic has
been light, a dream to drive in daytime, my foot
easy on the gas pedal.

"Back here in a fortnight Angel?"

"What's a fortnight?"

"Sorry, two weeks time."

"You gotta learn to speak English for god-
sake. Stay long enough and you'll wise up."

Her hand leaves my lap and searches the
glove compartment. Finding the stub of a pencil
and a scrap of paper she starts to scribble down
her telephone number. Missing the left for the car
park I make for the departure entrance. Stretch
limo's dress the forecourt, long, slick and a block
long. One day I'm going to try one of those babies
myself. A few drivers' heads rise as I pull alongside
– like who's the cowboy?

It doesn't take long to see Angel off. The
limo's are glad to see me go. Into third gear I
nudge back on to Paradise.

The drive back gives me more time to reflect.

I have spent what was left of the morning thinking out all the angles. In two weeks' time Angel's roll will be my bank roll. What kind of shit will come down on Angel? Who gives a fuck! If we had been pulled by the DEA last night, they would be ringing my bollocks right now, then shipping me back to the land of Nod. No, fuck you Angel. I'm going to hang you out to dry, make no mistake.

Tomorrow I'll phone Frank in London, I'll use Debbie's Sprint card. Tell him there is a package on the way and to wire me the money pronto. There are many loose ends to tie up in the next two weeks. I gotta call Debbie soon.

That girl Debbie, she is one of those loose ends. That beautiful chicano from Santa Fe. Could Debbie be the answer to my problem with Uncle Sam? Sure she could. It's me that's been saying no. But the longer I stay, the harder it becomes. From Immigration there is no escape. Ask any wetback. I sure as hell might as well be a wetback, even as a Brit. If I get caught, it don't wash telling them your mother got fucked by some Yank behind the Odeon picture house back in 1943. It doesn't work. Worst still, with the marriage stakes, you got to stay married for two years then report back to Immigration to obtain a full green card. Fuck! Two years in Vietnam must have been easier. These Yanks sure got a funny sense of humour. I'll call Debbie soon.

Five o'clock and Wayne and I ⟨...⟩
the wall. Wayne's pumping m⟨...⟩
mation on Angel, his old bald he⟨...⟩ ⟨...⟩k-
ing in anticipation. Wayne ain't seen no
hairy pie in years. I know this because he can't
stop talking about it. The less said about Angel
the better so I hand Wayne a can of Miller Light
and that does the trick.

An ageing prostitute joins us. I never saw
her before. I lean across Wayne. Fifty years and
sixteen stone or thereabouts and a real dog to boot.
She is now explaining the virtues of a fifteen dollar
blow job. For twenty-five you get the whole thing,
a shag with a rubber thrown in. Now you're talking.
"The rubbers 'cause I got an old man at home an' I
don't want him to catch nothin'." Hey, we got an
Aids campaign going on right here on the wall.
Give it another ten minutes lady, and you're going
to have an audience.

Steve and Tug join us. Tug has never been
called Tug before I met him. His surname is Wilson,
so it's Tug. As much as I explain that every one in
the British military has such nicknames, he still
casts a puzzled look every time it's mentioned.

I lean across Wayne for another look at the prostitute. Get real! I wouldn't touch that with your dick Wayne, never mind mine. Prostitution is illegal in Clark County, in which Las Vegas is situated. Most of the hookers walking the streets downtown are in her mould, older and past their sell-by-date. These are not the younger women who tip big to bell hops and bartenders to gain entrance to the better casinos. These girls never made the highrollers, even the escort agencies. Now it's a low motel room, the back of a car or somebody like Wayne, but then, Wayne's room will be safe. At ten o'clock when all her business is done, she will give her old man a miss and lay with Wayne. Wayne will be in the land of Miller Lights and she will go to sleep. Once again Wayne will be too pissed to take advantage and tomorrow I will hear his story of the hairy pie that got away.

My hand reaches for another can.

"Thinking hard John?" says Wayne in a whisper, trying his best to prompt a can from the box without making it too obvious. He gets his can and his smile tells me he's safe for the next fifteen minutes.

"Yeah, you could say that."

The beautiful chicano Debbie. The light-skinned American-Mex. Debbie lives on the wrong side of the tracks. Even in a small city such as Santa Fe, the wrong side of the tracks is the wrong side of everywhere. Well, me and Debbie got it together then the shit started to fly. Debbie's boyfriends are top drug-dealing no good bastards. That's who she lives with now and they're the people who ran me out of town and on to highway twenty-five south.

The talk has drifted to highways and byways, cities and towns that these men have drifted into then drifted out as fast.

"You ever been to Colorado John?"

"Just the once Wayne. I spent the weekend at the Charma fiesta in northern New Mexico. Camped ten miles north at ten thousand feet. Man! Clean air and breathtaking views. That was on the Colorado side Wayne."

"I know John. I was reared in a one-eyed town called Trimble, that's close to Durango. Anyways, I was raised around horses and cattle all my life. When I was ten Pa died, an' Ma, two sisters an' myself raised chickens. It didn't work out and I've drifted ever since and here I am an' it don't get any worse. If I didn't have this job I would be out on the streets."

I believe you Wayne. Without money in this, the richest country in the world, one might as well be living on a hill side in Peru.

"Say John, could you spare me a can?" Jesus! That was a quick fifteen minutes.

"Sure Wayne. Help yourself mate."

Tug reaches out and spins a dog-end at a passing Toyota high bed pick-up.

"Fuckin' Jap trucks man! They ain't got the steel in 'em like ours, hey Wayne?"

"Sure as hell no. I remember way back . . ." Here we go. My attention is diverted on to the corner of the block. Shit! Did I just see Jimmy scooting around the corner? Standing, I take a pace forward and take a long hard look. If that wanker . . .

"Where the fuck you goin' John?"

"No place."

"Well sit back down, I got a bone to pick with you Brits an' all."

I reckon Tug mustered education somewhere along the way. Some of his angles to situations border the extreme, but he's always got an angle.

"An' you people are gettin' my ol' State a bad name."

"What State's that then?"

"Goddamn Florida, finest State in the Union."

"That so! What the fuck are you doin' here then? I got it! Seen it on a licence plate one time "Will The Last American Leaving Florida Please Take The State Flag". It was you, weren't it Tug?" Wayne chuckles away but Tug has his back up.

"An' fuck you too cowboy! Just ride on out an' take with yer the horse you rode in on."

A dark blob of chewing tobacco is forced

from his mouth and slides into the middle of the road.

"Bad press, shitty press is what we're gettin' brother."

"How's that then?"

"Like this, man! Your young dudes is coming over with just hand luggage an' spendin' money, an' not too much of that. One week into the vacation, they fake a robbery. You name it, it's been stolen. Cameras, watches an' things you backward fuckers ain't even seen back home." He stops to place another stick of the foul chew between his teeth.

"It gets reported down at the station, the cops do diddly 'cept fill out paper work for travel insurance an' now we got another four innocent tourist robberies on the stats. Now, that ain't right, is it?"

"I think I'll go buy me some insurance right now."

"You make my balls ache man! Honestly!" Now there's a word that don't come easy on this wall!

Tommy, who is sat on the other side of Wayne is the youngest amongst us. I guess his age at twenty-two or three. I have never asked him. Anyway, he too is a resident and it's a little sad because to be living here in this pisshole means he is only two steps behind Wayne. But Tommy is an alright guy, so tonight I'm in good company but my empty stomach is rumbling and making its own conversation. Two cans later I make my leave. A shower and food beckons.

Within an hour I am back on the streets. I'll catch a meal down at Binnions later. Half way down the block and out of the corner of my eye I spot Tony. Worst still, he spots me. He has that long face of a man who has just stood in a pile of dog shit. Before he opens his mouth I know the story.

"How ya doin' Tony?" Need I ask! A shake of the head.

"I'm in the hole John. Any chance pal?"

"No chance Tony, I just ain't carrying. Got to fly mate. Take it easy."

He's in the shit. I just hope at the very least he has his rent money put aside.

Strolling the brightly-lit Fremont, I reflect on Tony's fall from grace. On the long road from Texas he's had his dreams. Tony hits the big time. Stretch limo's and highrollers. Gas pedal flat to the boards, he's heading west with the other twenty million people who visit Vegas with the same dreams. She attracts all the wrong kind. Drifters, gamblers, prostitutes, scam artists, you name it, it arrives, and a lot of it sticks. There is no other city like this in the world. Brash and mean she sucks you in then blows you out in bubbles. Look at Las Vegas this way: Caesar's Palace payroll is twice that of Rolls Royce motors. Just one casino, one attraction.

Tony rushes into town. He doesn't give himself time to settle down and find his feet. He is straight downtown looking for action in the smaller casinos. His first and biggest mistake. Thinking the action will be easy in the Ma and Pa games, he sits in. The retired old-timers have seen all this before. They have sat at these tables year in and year out. Patience is their game and slowly they milk Tony dry. Apart from patience, another discipline Tony lacks is temperance. Drinks don't cost a cent when you're sat down at the tables. The cocktail waitress hovers and it's all too easy to be looking into the bottom of a glass.

Tables are easy to get at nine p.m. The running buffet at Binnions is about the best value in town. This is an 'all you can eat' deal, and man it amazes me just how much food these Yanks can put away. They set about their six dollar 'all you can eat' like food is going out of fashion. Tonight the grub is up to scratch and in a smaller way I get my dollars' worth.

Downstairs on the casino floor, the noise is deafening. The slots rattle non-stop. Moving through the machines I slow down to watch the play at the blackjack tables. It's the croupiers that attract my attention. For a horny bastard like myself, these girls take some beating for looks anywhere. They say the most beautiful girls in the world work Vegas. I can well believe it. Every nationality is represented here. For some it's a stop on the road east from failed California dreams. But for most, the hustlers, this is utopia. They live in the fast lane looking for the one big pay off, the highroller who is going to whisk them off to greener pastures. Alas, most of them finish up more degenerate gamblers than the punters they ease the greenbacks from.

Moving forward I spot a stunner, a carnival-eyed Latino. Her slender hands deal the cards with lightning speed. The cards glide to a heavy Negro male who is drawing some attention. He is on a roll, the chips amount to about four hundred dollars. This might not seem a lot of money in terms of the millions of dollars each casino will turn over each day, but already the pit boss is hovering over the croupier's shoulder. He is fully aware that the punter will draw a flock of well-wishers to the table. Is this a diversion to attract attention from another table? Is this the prelude to a scam? How long has the croupier been employed by the casino? The pit boss switches the croupier to throw the punter's concentration. His eyes are glued to the Negro. The cocktail waitress somehow magically appears and now the punter will be drinking cocktails three times the normal house strength. All this is done with easy professionalism; decades of practice make everything flow unseen by the visitor.

Across the road in The Four Queens there is a quiet corner away from the machines and close to the reception area. A bank of telephones dress the wall and for some reason they are never in heavy demand.

"Hello Debbie, how are you doing?"

"Hey John! What the fuck are you calling me on this number for? You gone loco? Never mind this once, there is only me here. So, are you being a good boy for me Johnny? *Que si?*"

"Oh yeah. I'm always good for you Debbie, you know that."

"Oh yeah! Sure you are. You better be, hear me!"

"Can you get into town this weekend? It would be nice to see you again."

"Sure. Send one fifty to cover the flight. Get it to my work address on East Palace Avenue, you have the number. Right? The zip is 87505."

"Yeah, I got it somewhere. I'll Fed Ex it to be with you on Thursday. Ain't one fifty a little high? You rentin' a helicopter?"

"Aw Johnny, don't you be a cheap bastard all you life. You want me lookin' good, don't you?"

"Sure baby, sure."

"OK John. I will be in Albuquerque on Friday so I can take an early evening flight . . ."

"Great Debbie. I gotta run. Call me later with the flight details."

"Hey! Listen to me tea-bag head . . ."

I drop the hand set and exit Queens. That

girl could talk a glass eye to sleep! Nevertheless my jockey shorts begin to fill. That girl!

A single neon strip attempts to light the M1 corridor, the rest have blown, now collecting dust. An arc of light weaves its way across the carpet on to marine green walls. It's Wayne's door. It's open and it seems the boys are having a late one. I ain't going to break the light without being called inside to make up the numbers, and that's fine by me – I ain't got no plane to catch in the morning.

"Hi John, you're lookin' good. Step inside an' grab yourself a beer. They're on me tonight." Heavens Wayne! You been lucky today? Or just weighed those cans in?

"Sure mate, I'll be happy to."

Wayne's room has the same layout as mine. There is a difference with the decor though. Wayne being the maid-cum-cleaner, he has the perks of taking what don't belong to him when people move on and rooms are emptied. Picture prints hang his wall and suitcases pile the corner. He has two bedside lockers, so someone has none at all. Both have table lamps, and that says a lot about his status; lamps are only issued after one month's residency. Six ash trays and a television that works – so Wayne's proud as a peacock as he ushers me in. Tug's here, so is Steve.

There is one other guy making up the party. I've seen him around the building many times. He has never made the wall so we have never been introduced.

"Sit down John, sit yourself down. This here's George. You two know each other?"

"No, but nice to meet you George." George pulls me in with a strong, firm hand shake. Right away I know I'm going to like him. He couldn't be more different than the rest of us. George looks a well-kept sixty-ish, his tight, tanned skin and even teeth give a younger picture. Gold-rimmed spectacles rest along short, well-groomed greying hair. Manicured nails, light slacks and polished brown leather shoes. A sharp dresser. He's different. He's a player.

What's your story George? What brings you to live amongst fools and vagrants? He nurses a tallboy, leaning back against the plaster. Small talk rakes the room and Wayne has become the butt of jokes and piss-taking. He takes it all in his stride, casting long loving looks about his possessions. I sense this is well below George's intellectual level and before too long we are in conversation. How do I find the States? Its people? Its food? Its politics? My likes and dislikes.

"How long have you been here George?"

"In the motel? Six months I guess. It ain't too bad you know. I just need some place to rest day times."

"Day times? You work the graveyard shift somewhere?"

"In a way. I play the tables night time."

Looks like your breakin' better than even. What's the secret? What are you doin' here? He's already given a vague answer so I won't push it.

As cans pop, George keeps his tight to his chest, sipping a little now and again, completely out of character in this company.

"You make it pay?"

"I'm good. I got a lot of respect here you know. Every casino in this town, I'm good for a free comp." Comp means complimentary tickets, dished out by floor managers to regular rollers. It's a free meal, that's all.

"What's your secret? Gonna tell me?"

"Patience I reckon. You like to gamble John?"

"Back home, the ponies. Can't say I've been too lucky though."

"Luck! This town I've visited many, many times over the years. Let me tell you a story." He talks like he can fashion a story, his north-east accent is fast and crisp.

Cross talk between the rest has quietened some. George lights a Winston.

"Time ago, around your age, I walked on water. Two fine restaurants in New York, Syracuse china, Oneida flatware, piano bar, the works. I have people like Castellano over an' I'm turnin' a healthy buck. Atlantic City wasn't what it is today, so I would vacation down here two or three times a year. Nothin' big you understand, bring in a grand or two, enjoy the women, even brought 'em along some times. I knew them all. In fact one time, me and Paul gets blown by a hooker right there on Fifth in the back of a stretch. You believe that?"

I might, but the rest don't, showing their disbelief by slapping knees and sniggering.

"Let me tell the story. I'll take any questions afterwards. Right?" You have to do better than this George.

"Anyway, like I said. I'm ridin' high on the hip. What happens next? I gets me married up with a sweet thing half my age. Sells the business and moves down to California. Hey! I'm happy as a sand boy. Nice home on Laguna Beach. Nice wife who don't want kids and I open a deal right on the ocean."

There is only George talking now. He opens a can to lubricate his vocals, eyeing me keenly: am I a believer? You never know, even if it ain't true, it's a far better story than the rest of us could lump together.

"I'm closer to Vegas, it's but a drive. By now I get scared shit flying so my mileage is on the increase. I have good credit an' I'm welcome every place. The business is going great but things ain't too good at home. One weekend, going back fifteen years, I make town and room at the Sands. Come midnight I'm in my favourite chair, at my favourite table, playing the game I love best, baccarat. This night I have lady luck ridin' all the way with me. One o'clock I'm up one hundred grand, two o'clock, it's one seventy . . ."

"Hang on George. You're talkin' telephone numbers here. How much money did you take to the table?"

"Fifty grand. You think that's a lot eh? Come four o'clock I'm two hundred in front. You've seen nothing like it, the place is going crazy, there's management, dozens of 'em around me. It was the best, it beat sex any day."

Throughout Steve is the main disbeliever. Shifting around on the corner of Wayne's bed and shaking his head.

"Ain't that the biggest load of crock. Who the fuck do you think you got in here? The second grade? Get real!"

Steve has voiced the consensus. George is undeterred.

"The next thing I know, I'm in the best suite, I got champagne and dancin' girls. The next afternoon, I'm back at my favourite table. Everyone is waiting for me. Touch me! You're lookin' at a winner folks. And this is it: who the fuck do you think they got in the very next chair? Telly Savalas. Flown in there to build me up and shoot me down. They did. Eight hours later I'm down to my fifty stake an' calls it a day, and that's why I'm still good in this town."

"Telly Savalas eh? You might think he could be some place makin' a movie or something," says Tug.

Nice try George. It could work elsewhere, but here? Amongst the cigarette butts and empties? No chance.

"Telly owes 'em. They looked after him when he was startin' out. He's on call. They need a favour, an' he's jumpin' the next flight."

George edges off the bed and makes for the door.

"Give me five minutes boys, I'll be back." He's hardly out of the door when Steve speaks.

"That's the biggest pile of shit I ever heard. Whatever he's poppin' man, I hope to fuck he brings some back." Steve tosses his empty in the air. Wayne pokes his head round the door to see that George is clear.

"Bullshit is what I say. What do ya think John? You wuz listenin' most."

"I dunno. It's a wild story alright." Wayne places his forefinger to his lips. George enters the room clutching a brown envelope. He walks straight to me and sits down. Out on to the bed spill dozens of photographs. The restaurant. The beach house. He spreads them in a sequence and now it's a picture story. George, heavier and heavy with gold, smiling into the camera, his arms wrapped around a pretty blonde. Most of them show him and his wife, both of them look so happy. I believe you

George, but how can you still be in love with this town? Everything you owned is here and owned by some casino.

"Some story. But tell me, George, when you go back in the Sands these days – you know you've painted and papered the place – don't those old memories coming flooding back?" We both look down at the prints.

"I'm still good for a comp boys."

At eleven thirty I am back in room 105. It's the routine checks then lights out.

Stretched out on the thin mattress I ponder George's story. He made big with the free comp. It don't wash. Nobody is impressed. We all know there ain't no such thing as a free coffee, never mind a free lunch, in this city.

Blood red images dance and flicker along the white wall. The half open blinds let in the dancing neon from a burger joint one block east on Cerrillos. Darkness. Seconds pass, then blood splashes the walls again, lighting up the wall clock at the far end off the room. Her hands reach out to me. Three a.m. Debbie is lying tight besides me, her buttocks resting in the small of my back. Bright light screams through the blinds. Car headlights. Something is wrong. Engines roar and wheels are spinning. Two cars? Three cars?

My elbow takes the weight. Slowly I focus my eyes, looking down on Debbie. She shouldn't be here. Something is wrong. I rub the tousled hair that has fallen about her face. Wake Debbie. The motors purr but their lights throw long, dangerous shadows across the room. Move it Debbie! Outside the window I hear excited Spanish mumbo-jumbo, this ain't no friendly early morning shakes. It's Debbie's brain-dead boyfriends. Are two cars a show of strength? Or are there three of them? Move it Debbie! Crawling to the window, I shut the blinds. My heart is banging as I grope the floor searching out the snub nose .38. Shit! Where the hell are you? Where did I place it? Jesus! Of all times.

Outside, the wire-link fencing is whipping and screeching. Easing the lower blind I see three figures hanging and swinging off the link. Their mumbo-jumbo is now fever pitch. They're screaming Spanish insults. Debbie reads the picture, quickly pulling on her clothing. I look again, none appear to have shooters. Back on the floor, the shooter, where are you?

Debbie is at my side, pulling and tugging at my shoulder. The racket on the fence is getting louder. She stares into my eyes. There ain't no answers baby, you gotta go, get the fuck outta here. These jokers ain't going no place without you. Bitch is the only word I can make out. You gotta go! Debbie makes for the door. Not yet Debbie! Not yet, wait. Let me find the pistol first.

She is out of the door. It slams shut behind

her. The insults are now directed to her. Engines bark into life, a beam of light jerks across the blind. The last insults are for me, thrown from moving cars. Inglese bastardo. Loose gun fire aims at the moon. My heart is beating like it's going to burst right out off my chest. The .38 was lying in the fold of my trousers all that time.

Eyes pop open, eyeballs feeling the cold of the night. The crack dealers down the corridor are making trouble. I'm bathed in sweat and those bastards ain't going to get any quieter. It's going to be a long night. Yeah, Debbie walked out of that room like that's the way it is, sometimes the rules change, but in the end it's the same old game. You're right Debbie, and it's gonna be a long night because down the corridor the game is always the same.

"How ya doin' Frank? Me? I'm fine. Listen mate, I have some gear on its way to you. Yes, one watch. A gold and stainless Omega. That one stood me out a few bob mate, so I need a quick return."

I am talking from a call box and already I have people knocking to move me along.

"Right Frank. Cashier's cheque return of post. No Frank, I ain't seen no rain in months. Yes, I am a jammy bastard. Catch you later pal."

6.05 p.m. Friday night and I'm pacing the carpet outside gate twenty-eight on McCarren International. The flight is ten minutes adrift so I take a seat alongside the large windows and watch the departing visitors play their last quarters on the slots. Even here, just ten paces from the safety of the airliner, Vegas milks its last drop of blood.

Passengers start to filter through the gate. I stand on tiptoes trying to spot her tiny frame among the Stetson hats. There she is and what a picture. I guess Frank was right, I am a jammy bastard. She is the nearest thing I ever saw to a young Bardot. Those strawberry lips, parting and drawing back tight over white even teeth.

"Hello Johnny. You look smart. Is that jacket English?" I nod my head.

"And hello to you Debbie. Tell me, those tits, are they Spanish?"

A stupid reply I know. She smiles. Her lips draw back and the nostrils flare. It doesn't take a lot to get on the wrong side of that Spanish temper.

"Go fuck yourself John. Just you wait till I get you in that motel. You still living with all those dirty old men?"

"Yes, but then at least you know I'm safe. No women would come near the place."

"You better believe it Johnny boy. If there is any woman's shit in that room, I'll cut your balls off. Got it!" Shit!

"Let's get outta here."

"Drive me the Strip way. I want to see those beautiful lights again"

Her small suitcase sits squarely on her lap as the monorail speeds us on to the main terminal. I sit opposite. She smiles sweetly, her eyes slowly closing, saying don't look at me that way. Who are you kidding? Beneath that serene facade lies some wild, wild woman.

She sits up close besides me on the Chevy's bench seat. Her left hand rests gently on my shoulder. Her right hand lies on my thigh, the small finger making circles. Her nail scratches lightly on my skin. Moving off Paradise my hand slips down to change up a gear, then slips on to her hand and pushes it into my groin. She pulls away and slides over to the door.

"*Cochino!* Be a good boy, I have a nice surprise for you later." Debbie is full of surprises. So what is new.

In the short time since we left the airport, night has turned from blue to warm black. Caesar throws his neon into the night. Further down a volcano erupts, gushing flame that highlights Wayne Newton is still here and will be here for ever.

"Nice surprise eh Deb? Why not give it to me now? Go on Deb, right here in the truck."

She don't reply to that but rattles on at me all the way down the Boulevard. All of it going in one ear and out of the other. My ears will be black and blue. I just hope that's not the only thing that's black and blue by the end of the weekend.

Wayne made comment on my smartness as I left for the airport. It's Friday, isn't it? The boys are gearing up for a shindig and Wayne sees my absenteeism in absent cans. I need to park up away from the cocktail hour and sneak Debbie through the back door entrance. It would be twenty questions bringing her by the wall and, after Wayne has sunk a few, Angel's name could slip out and fuck up the weekend.

Debbie steps out of the shower. Her wet hair glistens like wet coals. The bath towel is folded high, pinching her small breasts. She sways from side to side allowing the towel to fall open along the front of her body. It opens up to expose her soft white belly. My eye follows the trace of fine hair from her belly button to the thick black curly bush between her legs. I move forward, she moves back.

"You want my pussy John. Ummm it feels so wet." Her hand moves down to grab and tug at her pubic hair. Her middle finger moves in and out of her body. Rejected, I sit back on the end of the bed.

"You want my surprise. Yes? Marry me tonight!"

"This some kind of joke. Since when the fuck did you have a sense of humour?"

"You no good bastard. Eight months ago you play with me in Santa Fe. Three times I fly to this shit hole. What for? You tell me?"

"You tell me Debbie?" She is really getting pissed off.

"*De marlo gusto!* You got two fucking ears right? Well listen. No licence, no pussy!"

My dick's telling me one thing; my brain another. But is this is the answer to my immigration problem? A green card for work purposes. Then again, I'm doing alright without one at this moment. Then again if I have to do it eventually, and whoever it is I'm going to get my ears chewed off, it might as well be Debbie.

"I ain't got no ring."

"Fuck the ring. You going to do it?"

What the hell, it's only a contract. After all, upwards of sixty thousand marriages take place here every year. So it's no big deal. Move over Joan Collins.

"OK Debbie, let's do it." I check the Rolex. It's nine o'clock. "There is plenty of time Deb. Come on, let's fool around a while."

"Call a cab now. No, none of that. No! Have I told you already, no. Now move it!"

"We don't need a cab. It's only three blocks away."

"Fine."

We walk Carson. Although only one block away from the brightly-lit casino area, the sidewalks here are dark and free of people. I know the way. I've walked past the Clark County Office many a time, but never to be married! We enter the building on South and Third. There has to be at least ten or twelve couples waiting in line after filling in the necessary licence details with the pencils provided. With some sixty thousand marriages a year taking place, that adds up to some pencils. In no time we are in front of a middle-aged woman. I don't know what title she carries – there must be one. She asks our full name, city we belong to and in Debbie's case, her age. Only because she looks younger than the legal age of eighteen years. I am asked for no identification, no nothing. Anyway, soon I am relieved of twenty-seven dollars and she punches our names into the computer.

Now we have the licence but we are not yet married. To do this you have two choices. One is a wedding chapel. That don't come cheap. The other is the Commissioner of Civil Marriages just across the street. The second choice appeals. An old-timer with a sympathetic face blesses both of us and a further twenty-five dollars seals the contract. Debbie has surprised me by being somewhat nervous throughout the short ceremony. I hope she is not taking all this all too seriously.

I am in need of a stiff drink.

"Well Deb, now I've made a honest woman out of you let's eat and fatten you up for the kill!"

"I am hungry John. We can eat and make plans for the future. Si?"

Jesus! We have been married half a block and already she's making plans.

"Let's make Fitzgerald's. The food ain't that great but at this time of night we'll get quick service."

We muddle our way through *tacos* and *enchiladas*. Debbie's idea. I am enjoying the Mexican beer better than the Mexican food.

"I will give two weeks notice, it's only fair . . ."

"What the fuck! Are you crazy? You want to live in this place? Look around you for fuck's sake, every bastard you see is wacko. Give me a break, I've been here too long already."

"So, clever person, any big notions?"

"OK. We could go *any* place."

"Let me know and I'll get my passport in order."

"You go back home Debbie. I will pick you up in Santa Fe next Sunday. I promise."

"You give *me* a break, dick brain. Why should I trust you? And what about the boys who will look for you if they know you are in town?" She looks at me disparagingly. She is not having any of this.

"They will kill you this time, make no mistake about that John. Greg says they will hang your balls out to dry."

"I'll take that chance. We'll be out of New Mexico within twenty four hours." She shakes her head. Her fork drops on to her plate.

"You're fucking crazy, I tell you. Santa Fe is so small. They will find you. Please let me come to you."

"Trust me Debbie. I will be there and everything will be alright."

If all goes to plan, I will be in the State of New Mexico one week Sunday – after skinning Angel.

Sipping *Margaritas* in the lounge of the Four Queens we watch an Elvis look-alike; it's a mediocre performance. The glitz and rapturous surroundings cover all sins and ills so he gets away with it.

I look into her eyes. Black as night, menacing yet inviting. Thick eyebrows highlight high cheek bones. She is a beauty. I have always thought myself a good judge of horse flesh and tonight, as I look around me, I sure have the pick of the paddock. She flashes her eyes along the bar, young bucks grin back. I am not alone.

"Let's go Deb."

Earlier in the evening I had picked up a handful of discount vouchers for the Days Inn. The discount is twenty-five per cent. The clean and spacious room at Days makes a welcome change.

Debbie takes a shower while I settle back on the king-size bed. Watching her undress, my eyes flicker between the cigarette I am rolling and the firmness of her young body. My tongue moistens the cigarette paper. As it strokes the paper, my thoughts are of it stroking somewhere else. The cigarette lit, I watch her slowly slide into the tub.

"Come and join me John."

Debbie draws her knees up under her chin to make room for me as I ease into the hot water. Her legs part and stretch, feet resting on either side of my chest, small delicate feet. My hands rest on her silky smooth thighs while her dark eyes quiz me and search for answers. She lifts her body and I feel her pubic bone rest heavily against my groin. Leaning forward I stroke the fine hair on the nape of her neck then pull her towards me, drowning in those large brown eyes, drowning in the warmth of her young tight body. Man o man! On a night like this a man could surely die a happy man!

I wake next morning sore and tired. Hours of passionate love makes my bell-end look like half a pound of streaky bacon. He begs me to ease him into the handbasin. Tepid water soothes the pain. Jesus Christ, I have another twenty-four hours of this to come.

"What are you doin' Johnny?" In the wall mirror I see her stirring, throwing the top sheet aside she stretches, naked, lean and mean. I close my eyes and look down into the basin; the old bobby's helmet looks a hopeless case.

"Speak to me Johnny. Come and wish your wife a good morning."

"Hang on a minute Deb. Just getting a brew on the go."

"*To* go, dick head! Come here."

"Bollocks."

I leave the kettle and gently wipe my groin and stroll over to the bedside. Bending, I kiss her belly, it has that musk smell from the long night of love making. The juices spilt hours ago are matted along strands of pubic hair and baked hard with body heat. Her hands stroke my face. They hold that same sensuous smell.

Both hands clutch the back of my head and

push it between her open legs. Her mound is sticky and in seconds it is wet, almost running with juices. My cock, which only minutes ago was in need of major repair, is now showing signs of a return to active service. I turn her over. She lifts her buttocks into the air. Parting them I slowly enter her, gripping her tiny waist. Her face rests on the pillow, turned and twisted.

I eventually make the needed cup of tea. The rolled cigarette burns deep into my lungs. Debbie waves the smoke in all directions, a non-smoker she gives an evil eye.

"That shit will kill you. A widow before I know it. What's the time?"

"Ten o'clock, well, near to. Why?"

"Why! Wake up. They are going to want the room at eleven. Did you leave your brain between my legs?"

"Ah fuck it, I'll book another night. You relax while I go down to the front desk. I need to check my room over at the motel anyway. It won't take but a hour. OK?"

"Bring me back a breakfast. A *taco* and French fries. Anything, see what they have."

I pay the charming receptionist with another discount coupon. Yeah, another cheap Brit on his wedding night.

The bright sunlight stops me in my tracks, but it's good to be out in the open air. I walk Carson keeping close to buildings and the coolness of the shade. Even the old M1 looks half tidy in the glare of the approaching mid-day sun. Wayne and a few unknown cronies sit infront of the motel making the place look untidy. Tony is amongst them. I ain't got the time to mess about with him this morning but have little choice as he is near enough blocking the doorway. On seeing me he jumps to his feet and stands out in front of Wayne's gang. Experience and instinct tell me trouble is afoot.

"How's your luck Tony? I ain't seen you in days."

I can see by his long face he is a day late and a dollar short.

"You got the ring John?" His feet are spread and firmly planted to the ground. Definitely trouble.

"You got the money?" I stop short, a good ten feet from him.

"I need the ring man. I'm headin' out tomorrow an' I need it for my ol' lady."

The ring is already in London. His eyes narrow. I'll bet he's given Wayne some bullshit about me, the ring and what he's going to do about it, because Wayne is perched to take whatever side comes out best.

"Sorry mate, it ain't with me anymore."

"What the fuck do you mean, it ain't with you anymore? You bastard!"

I cup my right hand to my ear, as if I am

hard of hearing. Tony steps forward. How many times has this ploy come to my rescue and worked. It looks like it's going to work this time too. Stupid bastard. I don't panic. In fact even at this late stage I still have my left hand in my pocket. Come closer. He stops within a foot of me. Hand still in pocket has confused him. I cup my ear once again. Leaning forward he does not see or even feel the initial pain as the top of my forehead crashes down into the bridge of his nose. Tony falls like a sack of shit in front of me. Now I free my hand, I bend over and drag him several feet alongside the motel wall. I leave him slumped against a dumpster. Tony is a pretty heavy guy but the dragging was made easy by his kicking and thrashing.

Women, money, even health may come and go, but respect once lost is lost forever. What would Wayne and his cronies have thought if I had backed down? Soft touch. Every bastard on the block would be walking all over me. Some things you just got to get right. Tony rolls on to his belly and attempts to crawl alongside the red dumpster. Two thudding kicks into his face and head bring him to a halt. Knowing it's futile to move, his blooded head sinks slowly into the dust.

Wayne's on my heels as I make my way into the motel. "You sure as fuck showed that motherfucker where it's at. I wuz about to tell 'im myself then you came along. That fucker's been a asking for that since he got 'ere." Tony has never harmed Wayne. He must think I came over on the last banana boat. Wayne is on the side of the dog that barks the loudest.

"I got me another place for the weekend Wayne. In the light of what has just happened, would you keep an eye on my room?"

"Sure thing John. You know you don't need to ask. I'm goin' to word the manager about that bastard . . ."

"There's no need Wayne. He's on his bike in the morning. Don't be arsed with it. Right?" Mike the manager wouldn't give a fuck anyway. He has enough problems with the crackheads and call girls. "Keep an eye on the room for me Wayne. Here's a ten spot. Get yourself some beer."

I take the rear exit out of the motel. The main reason being to avoid Tony. The guy is best left alone. Right to the end Vegas has been cruel to him. Now, where in the hell do you buy a *taco* from? Looking back I see Wayne and his cronies locked together in discussion. Wayne spots me and raises a hand. Where is the nearest *Taco Bell* food deal? You know, I don't think they have one downtown.

"What took you so long Johnny? No *tacos*, what's the deal?"

"I got you a cheese chilli burger with plenty of *salsa*, French fries and a side salad. Will that be fine for her ladyship?"

"Red or green chilli John?"

"Go to fuck, just eat the shit, this ain't downtown Santa Fe you know."

We eat the wedding breakfast in silence. Santa Fe may be a cosmopolitan city, but Debbie is anything but cosmopolitan. Street smart she may be but a conversation with a South American fruit bat would be more fruitful.

"Shall we gamble later John? Hey baby, get rich, maybe we buy that castle in England, what do you say?" She laughs out loud, the laugh and manner of a child yet the presence of a woman.

The croupier's eyes quickly fix on Debbie. Debbie taps the table, the cue for the dealer to slide the next card across the table. Debbie is happy with her two pictures and shows the open palm of her free hand. The dealer moves on, turns her cards only to bust with twenty-three. Debbie has had a nice little run of luck. The checks are lumped together but I guess there's around four hundred bucks lying in front of her. Well done Debbie. I guess you should be giving Tony lessons!

It's time to cash them in at the cage; it may never happen again! Debbie has the look of a dog with two dicks. Pleased isn't the word.

"What a blast man! I'm going to treat you now. Let's take a cab and find a good Mexican restaurant." We grab a cab on Fremont.

The rest of the day is spent fooling around

on the Days Inn king size and the old bobby's helmet does me proud. Late afternoon and she gets the need to return to her native city. I guess the bright lights of the big city have got to her. The airline is called and they say, sure, turn up we see no problems. That's it then. Honeymoon over. In a way, it's a relief. It's been a long time since I've had a woman this close for so long and in the end I'm making excuses to get away, any excuse to anywhere: checking the motel, stepping out to buy cigarettes, taking a piss. Another thing, all this time I have to make a major effort to accommodate her. *Are you OK? Can I get you anything? Don't worry about a thing. It will be alright.* It's doing my head. So in a way I'm glad to be seeing the back of her.

At the departure gate on McCarren the slots rattle a last goodbye.

"Well, it's *adios*. Be a good boy for me Johnny. Promise me you will be there next Sunday. Don't break my heart. You promise?"

"I promise. Now get your arse on the plane." She stands on tip toes, reaching up to me. Those soft warm lips brush mine and all rational thought begins to take off. Along with the aircraft if she don't move it. She moves away and is quickly out of sight.

Moving to the far end of the terminal, out of the large windows, I watch Debbie's flight taxi the runway. Its bright shiny skin sparkles in the sunlight. For a second Debbie stands motionless on the asphalt. Next she is roaring, sprinting, diving into the air to hurdle the grey brown mountains. Debbie shrinks to a dot. *Hasta la vista baby*.

GOODBYE ANGEL 5

"Two dollars and twenty five cents. Thank you for using Mountain Bell." I insert the coins and wait for the dialling tone in Reno.

"Hi." It's female but it ain't Angel.

"Is Angel there please? My name is John."

"No, she's not John, but she has left a message. You *are* the same Brit she met with in Vegas, right?"

"Yeah, it's the same one."

"Right. She says she will meet you as arranged. Does that make sense to you?"

"I guess so. What's your name?"

"Rose."

"Thanks a lot Rose. Have a good one."

"Nice talking with you John. You be careful . . . OK."

I look into the receiver. *Be careful.* Rose knows the score. Is she involved? Who is Angel running the dope for? How big is their operation? Who are these drug dealers? How big is their operation? Will we be followed? If I fuck up on Saturday night the consequences are going to be fatal. Drug dealers against a hot shot Brit don't make a match. A win for the home team.

The Chevy is parked out back of the motel. I am giving it the once over. Making sure the best I can that when I hit the gas pedal she blows me clear south into Arizona. Everything seems to be oiled and tight. Lights will be important, they all work. Belts are tight. Tyres at pressure. A windshield wiper blade needs replacing.

I am wiping my hands when Wayne meanders round the corner. Dropping the tail-gate I hop on and fashion a cigarette. Wayne comes alongside the pick-up and fails in his attempt to swing himself up. In desperation he mounts the rear wheel and pulls himself over the pickup's side. He's huffing and puffing like he belongs with the three little pigs.

"Been a call from London, John. Mike told me to tell you." He is struggling for air but he lights up all the same.

"I've been expecting one. Is there a message?"

"Says you're *weighed in*. Fuckin' limeys." He gives me a strange look.

I know what it means alright. A cashier's cheque is waiting for me at the First Interstate Bank on Fifth. Wayne is given a five bill and slides off the tail-gate, heading off to the Seven-Eleven for a six-pack. His face, screwed with pain, shows the ordeal he is going to face remounting the tail-gate on his return.

"Hey John, there's a broad on the telephone. Right now!"

It's Mike, the manager. Although small in stature his little legs go off at ten to the dozen so I have a job keeping up with him.

"That you John?" The office is small and I notice they have my name spelt wrongly on the key board. That could be an advantage.

"Hey Angel, how ya doin'?"

"Swell baby, looking forward to seeing you tomorrow night. I'll be coming in on Greyhound so I'll call you when I get in. OK?"

"You know the bus depot's right here downtown?"

"I do honey. Catch you later."

Mike looks at me with despair, that universal look between men when they feel one of their own kind is under threat from the opposite sex.

"Everything alright John? Was that the blonde that came by some weeks ago?"

"Yeah. The very same. Why?"

"I don't know. I'm sure I've seen her around before. Just can't put a match to it. You be careful that's all." He's stroking his chin as he follows me out of the office. *Be careful* once again. "You seen Wayne? I'll bet he's loaded again. What am I goin' to do with him? By the way, your television'll be fixed Friday." Rent day. I believe you.

The rest of the week has been spent tidying up loose ends. Documents like my passport have been wrapped and sealed in envelopes. Driving documents will be kept on hand for the drive out. My best clothes have been folded and packed in cases and boxes. Old clothing has been left lying about to give that lived-in appearance. This is not only to give Angel that impression but nosy Wayne also. The need to get her pissed is greater this time so two bottles of spirits are already in position under the washbasin. One with her tipple, Kentucky whisky. A bottle of white rum stands alongside, half drunk by Wayne earlier in the week; it has now been topped up with water. That will be mine.

I will need to be reasonably sober on my drive out of town. I plan to drive High Ninety-Three south and head for Kingman, Arizona. Thirty miles outside Vegas the highway narrows down to two lanes. One of the worst accident black spots in the States, it attracts constant police activity. I will drive ten miles south to Sam's Town then park up behind the Nevada Palace hotel casino. In amongst the hundreds of parked cars I will catch up on my sleep then wait 'til sun up before moving on.

Angel telephoned the motel around five leaving a message that she would call by around eight. The alarm clock tells me it's eight thirty and apart from last minute checks around the room I am fired up and ready to go. She's late and for a moment my arse hole begins to twitch, then there's a knock on the door.

"Hey John, that blonde's outside. Honest man! Right out there on the wall. She's askin' for you, you lucky bastard. I sure wish I could have a piece of her ass." The look on his face tells me he is in need of it.

"Cheers Wayne, tell her I will be out in a minute."

Yeah Wayne my old mate. If in the morning you can catch her, you can grab all the arse you like, but when she wakes she'll be doing sixty miles an hour through the motel.

I follow Wayne out of the corridor. Angel is sitting on the wall with a couple of tail-enders from the cocktail hour. I boot an empty can across the parched grass. Losing your touch Wayne; am I making you lazy? Angel raises the beer can to me.

"How you been John?" The people on the wall I don't know and looking at them I don't want to know.

"Come and join us John, these guys . . ."

"Let's go Angel, I don't fancy sitting down at the moment."

The two middle-aged whites sat next to her I have never seen before. They both look regular pissheads but they could be anybody. How long have they been here? Better still, who are these guys? Where do they belong?

"Over here Wayne." Wayne's dithering about again, looking to take sides. He rolls over to me.

"Who the fuck are these people Wayne? And where do they come from?"

"I never seen them before. Honest." That word again.

"You never seen these guys before? You kiddin' me?"

"On my old mother's grave, God bless her soul."

"Come on Angel, let's go."

What the fuck are you playing at Angel? You of all people should know better, mixing it with people like that. And there is something I don't see. The shoulder bag!

"Any plans for tonight John? I need to know."

"No. Should I be making plans with you coming into town?"

"OK, listen. I have to meet with my ex again, same deal as last time. Is that alright with you?"

"That's fine with me. Let's take a cab from the Queens."

"He's late with the alimony again."

"Hey! You don't have to say a thing. Whatever you have to do is fine by me."

"Be lucky you guys," says Wayne shaking an empty.

"Be lucky Wayne? If I fell into a barrel full of tits I would come out sucking my thumb!"

Wayne laughs while Angel pulls me off in the direction of Fremont.

The bag Angel? Where's the fucking bag?

The cabbie leans his head sideways, his open palm asks the question.

"We need the Tropicana. But before that I need to call in at an apartment on Main." He nods and releases the cab door handle to let us in.

One mile down Main and he makes a left into the apartment complex. This ain't the best of places so he parks under good lighting. Angel takes off into the block.

"Be back in a second honey."

I open the rear door and light up a cigarette. The taxi's engine is still running; the tobacco smoke drifts into still air. The cabbie turns towards me.

"You're from Australia. Right?"

"No."

"Well, wherever you fuckin' come from, close the door man!" I flick the cigarette into the dust and close the door.

"Got to be careful man. We got three drivers shot to death this month alone. Hey, I'm looking out for you as well. Am I right?"

"You're right."

"So tell me, where are you from?"

"England."

"Really! What brings you to Vegas?" I get to look at him: Anglo, middle-aged, heavy set and in need of a shave.

"Just to visit. How long have you been here?

Was you born here?"

"Born here man! I don't believe anybody is born here. Hell no. I drifted in to town some eighteen years ago. Same dreams as every other guy. Here I am: fat wife, three kids and twelve hours a day stuck in this cab. Tell you man, life's a bitch and then you die!"

He makes a quick call to his office.

"Where did you drift from?"

"Rapid City, South Dakota. You ever been there?"

"No."

"Don't fucking bother and do yourself a favour."

"I bet you have seen some changes in eighteen years?"

"You bet! Everything is so tight today. Years ago when the mob had its say, payin' for cocktails at the bar was unheard of, now accountants run the show. You know what I mean by the mob?"

"Yeah."

His fingers start to drum the dash.

"Where the fuck has she got to?"

"She won't be much longer – her kid sister just dropped a baby." Some excuse. Where the hell are you Angel?

"Look man! It ain't the meter you understand, you guys are payin' the tab anyways. It just ain't too healthy around here." For fucks sake hurry it Angel. I am getting nervous myself.

No sooner thought than Angel appears out of the darkness. Her jacket is slung over her left shoulder. She slides into the rear seat. The jacket drops off her shoulder, a bulky shoulder bag follows. Bingo! The driver, I never asked his name, heads back up Main and takes the ringroad skirting the city. Angel's hand reaches for mine, the palms are sticky with sweat. The bag is stuffed between her legs and I can feel the tension in her body. A slim gas lighter shakes on to the tip of a cigarette. That bag ain't going no place.

To keep the routine simple I head for the same bar as last time. I order up, then Angel takes off in search of her ex. Soon I am making small talk with two young fillies from San Francisco. They are interested in England while I am interested in them. Suspicions are always aroused when two of the same gender travel together from faggot city. They are both Anglo. Jane is slim and attractive while Kelly is short and fat, a real dog and a living example of Darwin's theory. Still, I'm not in the market for hairy pie. Tonight that runs a definite second to the main menu. Money!

"Hi honey, sorry it took so long. Some mix-up about his break. Order me a large scotch will you?"

I order the scotch and take stock. Angel is more relaxed this time, no sudden dash for the exit door. The bulky shoulder bag has been replaced by a smaller one. The two west coast girls ease into the conversation. Jane cannot take her eyes of Angel's tits. I wonder if Angel would be into that scene. Any night but this it might interesting to find out. I turn away and let the girls talk between themselves.

The trio on the small stage strikes up, a pretty girl in Western dress adjusts her yellow bandanna then lays into an old Patsy Cline number, *San Antonio Rose*. She is a real singer, then she would be. At ten o'clock it is that time of the evening when it's catch 'em and hold 'em. The girls talk on. I catch city names and strange games. I dismiss top shelf thoughts and this time it's me that says it's time to go.

Fremont at midnight *is* Las Vegas. Masses of people criss-cross the street, hopping from one casino to another. We alight from the cab and step on to the street of dreams, and why not? Tonight when Lady Luck shines down on me, Vegas just this once will smile for me.

We enter Binnions Horse Shoe through the side entrance. The main doors are being picketed by the Culinary Workers' Union. Despite the union, the place is as full as usual. Why has Angel chosen here? The security has been doubled since the picketing began two days ago. Was it Angel's choice of rendezvous? This meet must have been arranged last week before the strike action. No, this a fuck up. They have dropped a right bollock. Television cameras surround the building at all hours. Jesse Jackson gave a speech out front to two thousand people three nights ago. Angel's people could not have picked a worse place for the drop.

"I got to use the rest room honey. It won't take too long."

My eyes don't leave her back as she walks off to check the plumbing. If she doesn't make her contact where does that leave me? Is she going to throw a wobbly and jeopardise my plans? Then again, if she does not make contact just how much money will she be carrying back to the motel?

She is back with a face like a smacked arse. I see nothing is going right for her and fear she may be thinking foolish thoughts. She's had a fair bit to drink and I know it's going to require all my skills to nurse her back to the motel.

"Drink your scotch. Is everything alright?"

"Yeah, let's make it quick. This place is giving me the hump!"

I have to take the initiative.

"Hey! Hang on a minute Angel! Just what the fuck is going down? I take you out for the evening and all I'm getting is shit . . ."

"I'm sorry John, but my ex is giving me hell over our daughter. Shit! Come here." She leans over and kisses my cheek.

Angel is running out of options. OK, let's assume she has missed her contact in Binnions. She has pockets and a handbag stuffed with cash. Where at this late hour can she go? Who can she trust? Especially when she's carrying all that money? She can go to a hotel room perhaps? She might not feel too safe on her own though. The answer is she can go nowhere and trust no one. It's trusting either me or the bunch of niggers who will be trading drugs outside the M1 about this hour. I think I got the edge.

The midnight air is cool and refreshing. Angel has been throwing the scotch back like there is no tomorrow, but she is still walking a straight line and I have to play the straight guy.

"What do you fancy doing Angel? A meal perhaps?"

"I'm sorry, let's take a bottle heh. And go back to your room?"

"I got some booze in on the off chance, save us going to the liquor store. It won't do me any harm anyway. I feel like I need an early night." Like one a.m is early!

"There's something I got to tell you John, I got woman's problems, you know, it's that time of the month. You ain't mad are you?"

I guess she cannot see my half smile in the darkness of Carson. I look to the heavens, the stars have come out to play. Man! I should be selling double glazing.

"I understand Angel. Let's get back, get comfortable and open a bottle."

"You're some guy, you know that?"

"Pour a stiff one for me honey, will you?"

This will be Angel's fifth glass. God knows where she puts it. She started off sitting on the bed with her back resting against the wall. With each glass of bourbon she has slid farther down the wall and is now slumped on one elbow. Her shoulder bag is slumped alongside the waste pipe of the handbasin. It's all down to Father Time now. Please Father Time, make the next twenty-four hours speedy and fruitful.

Angel is soon out of the picture, fully-clothed and sound asleep. I edge along the bed and stroke her hair. She is dead to the world. Rolling a cigarette, my eyes focus and stay on the bag. My heart beats hard as I drag the bag towards me. Now I got my fingers crossed, legs crossed, toes crossed, everything crossed.

The bag feels light but bulky. Zipping it open, some of the contents spring out on to the floor. Greenbacks. It is stuffed tight with greenbacks. I look back at Angel. She has stirred, but only to turn on her side.

I spew the contents on to the floor, spreading the notes into dollar strengths. The one hundred bills are making the biggest pile, twenties a close second and there is small change in the way of ones. Thirty rolls are rubber-banded, each one contains one thousand dollars. *This is something else*. My heart is beating harder and my hands are shaking. My troubled hands roll another cigarette. One thousand dollar stacks: eighty-five, eighty-six, eighty-seven thousand dollars! Jesus Christ! The smoke fills and tugs at my lungs. Sweet Jesus! I refill the bag and throw it back alongside the waste pipe. I can't believe it: eighty-seven thousand smackaroos right there at my feet. Well Debbie, it sure looks like I'll be arriving in style.

It is time for quick, positive thinking. Angel is comatosed, so she ain't no problem. But is the motel being watched at this very moment? Have we been followed? If Angel's people know my movements they will know of my pick-up out back, surely that will be being watched. I cannot risk the truck. What the fuck, a fifteen hundred dollar vehicle ain't going to bust me now. I will leave it behind. The only other means of escape out of this marooned city is via the airport, and that's the way I gotta go.

Reaching up, I pull down my travelling holdall from above the makeshift clothes rail. Quickly looking over the top contents I lift out the essential travelling documents: passport, driving licence, First Interstate bank ID card and automated teller card, and social security card carrying the words "not valid for employment". These have been checked over and over again in the past week. I place them in a small travelling bag, the shoulder type that will accommodate both my documentation and Angel's cash. Reaching over to the bedside cabinet I remove the .38

and proceed to wipe it over and over with a tea towel.

Sat on the floor, my back arched against the bed, I look over at Angel, then at the threadbare curtains, the knackered air conditioning machine, the stained carpet, the "I'll fix it Friday" television. I'll bet my bollocks this room ain't seen so much money. Then neither have I. The money is transferred into my bag. The revolver is tucked on top of the money and the bag is zipped.

Checking Angel is still comatose, I open the door to the corridor. For once the dope heads are out of the building or out of their heads 'cause I don't hear them making a racket. That's one plus, now I just hope to Christ the payphone outside Wayne's room is in working order. First I check the rear entrance. I open the door a couple of inches and peer into the darkness. I can't see a lot, only, by the driver's side of my Chevy, another vehicle parked alongside and behind, and the still of the night.

I close the rear door and draw the top and bottom bolts to lock it. The door was replaced in the week. Tough luck if there's a fire tonight campers!

"Northern Lights taxis. Can I help you sir?" She's working.

"Send me a cab to the M1 on Sixth. How long's it gonna take?"

"No more than five minutes. Where is the destination sir?"

"The Mirage. Tell your man not to leave the cab or sound his horn, I'll be waiting outside for him."

"Be right with you sir. Thank you for using Northern Lights."

The room gets the final once-over. I cover Angel with a blanket to keep her warm against the cold night air. My heart is pumping. Sweet dreams baby. I know the next five minutes are critical; I just got to hope that if I am being watched, it's the truck they will be watching. It's shit or bust time now. I wait behind the main door listening for the sound of the cab's motor. Minutes later the cab's headlights throw shadows through the window lights on each side of the main doorway.

Here we go. Five steps and I'm at the taxi's door. Without a word I open it swiftly and sling my case and holdall along the rear seat – I am quickly in behind the driver.

"Mirage. Right my man?"

"Right." Get the fuck outta here now. It seems like a lifetime before the cab slowly leaves the curb. My heart's missing beats and my arse hole is twitching. When the fuck are you going to get this motherfucker into third gear!

We turn left on to the Boulevard. Looking over my left shoulder I see that nobody is giving chase. I also catch a glimpse of the pick-up, the street lighting reflecting off its roof. It's a shame to leave her but, come the morning when the shit hits the fan, someone may figure that if the truck is still in town then I may be too, hiding in some motel away from the downtown area. This ploy could give me valuable time – days, even a week to break clear out to New Mexico.

I dropped a right bollock when I let Debbie give her home city and State to the computer when we got married. Anybody with half a brain will make the connection between Debbie, Santa Fe and myself. Still, what's done is done, it's time now to get the hell out of here.

"Here on vacation huh?" We are well away from the motel now and I feel a bit more relaxed.

"Yes, you could say that. Could you make it McCarren please. I've changed my mind."

"McCarren! Some change my man. I gotta call in."

The airport looms large in front of us. The driver's done a good job and kept his mouth shut most of the way.

"Thanks for the tip man, most appreciated. Heh! are you Australian?"

Fuck off!

A short walk and I am inside the terminal building. I need to off load the .38 before I approach the ticket desk. The problem I have is that these waste bins are emptied whenever, and whenever could be five minutes after I hide it in there. That would cause a major predicament, the whole caboodle would be swarming with cops in no time. I look and find the car park exit door. Five minutes later I am out on the lot. Finding a dark corner, I dig the revolver into the hardened earth. I cannot afford to hang around, so a half-hearted effort is made with the burial. Still, it's covered now. What possessed me to bring it in the first place I will never know. The first winds will uncover it.

"The first available flight to Albuquerque please."

"Two thirty this morning sir. If you would like to make a reservation that will be eighty-six dollars. Would you like to book sir?" She don't look up.

"I'll take it."

"Thank you sir for flying South West. Here are your boarding cards. Gate eighteen is on the other side off the airport . . ." She is about to give me more details but I politely cut her short; I would like a dollar for every time I've played the last slot machine in Las Vegas before showing a boarding card. People are always helpful when they hear the limey accent; this morning I don't need help. Feeling the bulk of the shoulder bag against the side of my body, right now all I need is a cup of strong black coffee and some luck.

"This better be fuckin' good John – you got any idea of the time?" Debbie sounds in good form. What's new?

"Yeah, I wear a watch. Listen Debbie, meet me on Albuquerque airport at four thirty your time will you?"

"Will I! Will I fuck! Where's the pick-up? What are you doing on an airport anyway? Where are you?"

"Don't give me a hard time, be at the airport."

"I'll give you a hard time if you call this number again this morning. Tell you what Johnny, call me when you make Santa Fe. *Bueno noches.*"

"Bollocks!"

All the time I am on the airport I can't relax, pacing up and down the terminal, believing that once airborne all will once again be calm. No such luck. Although I am putting mileage between Angel and myself the flight is a nightmare. I just cannot let go of the shoulder bag, clutching it like I'm about to

lose it the same way I found it. I am knackered but
dare not fall asleep. I feel once in the land of the
dead I may never wake again.

"The first shuttle bus to Santa Fe leaves at
nine a.m. sir. It's called Happy Jack and will cost
you nine dollars fifty. Your first time in The Land
Of Enchantment sir?"

I look up. Yes, this is the airport tourist
information desk. I tell her it isn't my first time.

"All the same sir, enjoy your stay in New
Mexico. The Happy Jack leaves outside the main
exit. Have a nice day."

I have three hours to burn before Happy
Jack arrives. What a pisser. I don't want to phone
Debbie. It would be a waste of time, and anyway I don't think I could stand all her moaning and groaning at this early hour. More black
coffee.

Under a clear blue sky Happy Jack pulls
himself north on Highway Twenty-Five. He will
climb and, two hours later, he will be purring at
a little over seven thousand feet before he settles
on the high desert plain nestled below the beautiful
Sangre Mountains, backdrop to the oldest city in
the Union. I know this old city well: its streets and
its people. Is Debbie awake? Who was she sleeping
with last night?

The shuttle bumps along. Scrub bush on
brown and red soil on either side. Sagebrush
and Mesas. Indian country this, road signs tell

me so. Pueblo settlements are named every mile or so. I read the signs but before I can begin to pronounce the name another looms.

Pulling the bag in closer, I try to deliberate Angel's dilemma. She could still be crashed out . . . no, Wayne would have given the door a knock by now. Poor cow, but then fuck her. She is history now. In the distance I see Santa Fe and begin to warm to the visit. There have been happy times in the past. The driver drops me on Cerrillos.

"Hi Jeff, howya doin' pal?"

"Hey John! How's Vegas, is it all working out for you?"

"It did but at the moment I'm calling from the Thunderbird Inn on Cerrillos, not too far from your office."

"I'll be darned! Why are you back in town? Is there a story?"

"You could say that."

"I'll bet."

"You still got that safe in the office, Jeff?"

"Sure, do you need to use it? It's not dope is it?"

"No Jeff. I wouldn't drop you in the shit. You know that?"

"I don't see a problem then."

"Great. Where shall I meet you? At the office?"

"No John, walk up to Burger King. It's north

on the same block. Give me twenty minutes. Hey! congratulations, Debbie called by the office – old married man now heh?"

"Can't be happy all your life!"

"Hmm. Twenty minutes John."

Jeff lives twenty miles south in Lamy. The twenty minutes driving time gives me time to organise my room. I'll take a shower when I get back. I still cannot take my eyes off the money bag. I'll sure be glad when it's all put to bed in Jeff's safe. For now, I walk it down to the front desk. The old geezer who welcomed me in moves it into the back room of his office. Several times he lifts the weightless case in the air and gives me strange looks. Is this guy winding me up? It's empty, ain't it? Empty it ain't pal. Sit on it, lean on it, sleep on it, do everything you gotta do, because inside is all I got. All I got besides three grand I'm carrying on my hip.

I settle into the red vinyl booth. The French fries are predictable but the double cheese chilli burger is pretty good, but then, don't we Brits own the business now? I have not seen Jeff since I left Santa Fe four and a half month ago. Jeff has a restaurant supply business not too far from here. Like most business men in this town, he is from out of town: San Dimos, California. And like most west coast people he's as sharp as a razor. He also has a rare American attribute, a sense of humour. A black Mazda pick-up swings on to the lot.

"Hey John! Tell me you're keeping out of trouble. Right?"

"Right now, yes. How's the family Jeff?" We shake hands then Jeff sits opposite.

"They are in great shape. Tell me the story John?"

"And business Jeff, how's business?"

"That's in great shape too. The story John!"

"I got a little lucky so I need to stash some cash."

"How lucky? How much is a little?"

"Eighty seven grand, and I got four of my own."

"Sweet Jesus! You need a bank. Vegas don't let you walk away with that kind of money John. There is a story isn't there?"

"The one that got away. Yeah, I'll tell you back at the office – I got to be careful, you understand?" His head nods, real slow.

"I understand. Have you seen Debbie since you've been back?"

"No, I wanted to get this business out of the way first. I don't know if she should know anyhows."

"She would sure help you spend it. Right?"

"Right."

"I don't see the Chevy on the lot John, is it back at the motel?"

"Blew the block would you believe?" I can see he ain't believing none of it. He knows how much that old truck meant to me.

"Come on John let's go, I got the old lady on my back these days."

Five minutes later we swing off Cerrillos and ride by the Thunderbird where I pick up the bag the old geezer's been keeping for me. Inside a gear change we are outside the office.

I place the bag inside the safe.

"Here is the key John, and a key to the main door. You know the alarm system so you ain't got no problems. How long do you figure you will need it?"

"A couple of days most, then I'll be down the road."

"I'll have to keep Maxine outta there that's all. I don't want anyone knowing I have that kind of money lying around."

"I sure appreciate this, Jeff . . ."

"Tell me what's gone down, you have to be honest with me John, I'm putting myself on the line for you."

I go through the story. He looks at me in disbelief.

"John! I'm telling you, every story gets worse. You listen, and listen good. You got to get the fuck right outta this country, not the state, the country. You ain't going to make it out alive. Look at all the shit that went down with Debbie's gang last time. Somebody is goin' to shoot you. Believe it!"

"I always get the breaks Jeff, you see."

"And boy are you gonna need 'em! Do me a favour John, don't be too long sorting out this business in Santa Fe. It ain't looking too good for you and I don't want to be mixed with anything heavy." He looks at me with disapproval, disappointment even. He doesn't really want this and can I blame him.

"I gotta go. Do me another favour and call Debbie now will you? If she finds out you've been here and not called, my life will be hell. Do that for me uh, and be careful."

"Hi Debbie, how you doin'?"

"Where have you been John? All morning I have been waiting for you to call me. Where are you now?"

"I'm with Jeff at the office. I am booked in at the Thunderbird on Cerrillos, you know it?"

"I know it. Have you forgotten something?"

"Love you Deb."

"You bet Johnny, and don't you forget it."

"Right, see you at four o'clock?"

"Gonna need your strength John. I would get plenty of rest if I were you." I put the receiver down and turn to Jeff.

"Need your rest eh John?" Jeff must have heard the conversation.

"It's the old adage Jeff. For the first four weeks you wish you could eat it, for the next forty years you wish you had."

"You're a fucker, no mistake. Do you need a ride John?"

"Thanks Jeff, but no. I need to see someone on the way back to the motel."

A flea market stands on Cerrillos, just short of and opposite the Thunderbird. It is only a small market, playing second fiddle to a larger one north of the city. That is of no consequence because I know the person I need will be on Cerrillos. A strong wind is starting to blow from the south, flapping awnings and making stall-holders busy rearranging their displays on their trestle tables, saving the lighter goods from take-off. Dust swirls amongst the caravans and trailers. At first I don't make out the rig I need. The wind dies and the dust settles. Squinting, I see Bill's rig at the far corner of the lot.

"How are you doin' feller? Hey Ma, look what the wind blew in." Old Bill steps back into the trailer. "What on earth are you doing here? Last time we seen you, you were headin' out to Vegas."

"Just made it back Bill." Bill's wife pokes her head out of the door. She doesn't remember me.

"What can I do for you feller?"

"I need a shooter Bill. What you got?"

"Step inside. Ma will put the tea on. We drink tea all the time you know, less caffeine."

I follow him into the trailer. It is well laid out and practical. Bill is a retired army officer and he travels all over the south-west trading at flea markets. Soon they will drop down into Albuquerque, trade a few weeks then chase the sun, west into Arizona then north to Nevada. He is a good hustler but he always tells me his pension saves many a day.

"Enjoy your stay in Vegas? Me and Ma will make it out there come November. We go every year, don't we Ma? We do just dandy." Bill taps the burnt remains of his pipe into a china dog bowl.

"What are you looking for, feller? Is the tea made, Ma?"

"Same as last time, you know? Something light, I ain't too bothered about the velocity, a .38 will do so long as you have the right ammunition. Can you do that?"

Bill moves to the end of the trailer and reaches up on to a shelf.

He pulls down several hand guns. It is not illegal to sell firearms on a flea market in New Mexico. There are guns on the tables outside but I feel it to be prudent to choose inside the trailer, although I know it is going to cost me more for discretion. Ma checks on the stove and opens the trailer door to cast a sharp eye upon their ware.

The old lady moves over as Bill moves closer

with the arsenal. I know the piece I want. It needs to be small, size doesn't bother me. The same .38 calibre I just buried in Vegas will fit the bill because if and when you have to shoot these things, the first round away may be the frightener, but the second round goes right to the head. Pull the trigger twice and blow the fuck away. Always two rounds minimum. Speed is always essential so I will want a double action, no safety catch. Just point and shoot.

This isn't to say I am about to rekindle the Lincoln County Wars. The next twenty four hours could turn a mite nasty and if Greg comes after me mob-handed, at the very least I have a frightener. The old lady comes over with the tea.

"How about this one feller? This one will fit you."

It is a .38 Rossi. I handle the pistol, checking for tightness and condition. She's in good nick. Tomorrow morning I will fire her at the Buffalo range on Airport Road. Until then I will have to take Bill's word. I'll bet my bollocks he ain't never fired it.

"Fired it myself only last week."

"She feels fine Bill. What's the deal?"

"One thirty an' I'll throw in the holster and a box of hollow points." If the worst scenario should take place, it's a hollow point round that wants to be discharged from the business end. "You got a right good deal there feller."

"Sold. Let's drink some tea."

Leaving the flea market I look to the skies: dark ominous clouds are sailing at speed, rolling menacingly low. They are waiting for me to make open ground before they spill their contents. I hurry on, the .38 stuck down my waistband, the butt concealed by my jacket, which is threatening to be torn off my back by the strength of the wind. I lengthen my stride, one eye searching out the Thunderbird Inn, the other to the black sky.

Within seconds of closing the motel door behind me, the heavens open. The slamming of the rain on to the hard baked arid earth is deafening. Within minutes the land south of the motel is awash. Peering through the window at the show outside is better than television. The six lane highway is deeper than the Rio Grande. All vehicles are stalled, the water racing past at door-handle level, their occupants standing on car hoods or wading for high ground. Some of the lighter cars are slowly moving behind the force of water. The speed at which the water level has risen is something else. Talk about Manchester. I ain't seen anything like it since monsoons in Malaya.

My outside interests are interrupted by hammering on the door. I check my watch: three forty-five. It must be Debbie.

"Jesus! Just look what the cat dragged in."

She is standing in the doorway like a

drowned rat. I am surprised that I am not confronted by a tidal wave as I open the door, but no, the motel must be on higher ground than I thought.

She pushes past me, the water running off her on to the carpet.

"Do not say another fuckin' word. Boy! Am I pissed. Once in a blue moon this shit comes down and you have to pick the very day. You do my tiny head!"

She starts to discard her wet clothing. In no time she is naked and climbing in between the sheets. Shivering, she pulls the blankets tight around her neck.

"Just keep your distance lover boy – a lot of explaining you got to do. Where's the pick-up?"

Fuck me, meet the wife. In the door two minutes and she's at my throat. I must have a weird sense of humour, because ever onwards I will be taking it up the arse from this girl, minus Vaseline.

"It broke down outside Vegas."

"I do not believe you."

"Believe it or not I don't give a shit, but as your pretty eyes will tell you, it sure as fuck ain't on the parking lot."

"Well clever dick for brains, you got some strange notion of me walking about this planet for ever more."

"I'll buy us a motor in the morning."

"No kidding. You got yourself rich, right?"

"Give me a break Debbie. We're gonna be alright. Don't worry about a thing."

"We are going to be OK heh? How much we got then?"

"When I know you better I'll tell you."

She bolts upright ready to give me some verbal. I look at her exposed breasts and wink. She snorts and quickly covers herself.

"I need you along tomorrow."

"To buy a car! What do you need me for?"

"Let's say it's a wedding present. You register it, then it's yours." Her little face lights up. I don't want my name on any hick computer. No trace.

"What's the catch Johnny?"

"There ain't no catch. I'm trying to do good by you and this is what I got to take."

"I want a red Cadillac with red leather seats and . . ."

"Hang on Debbie. Fifteen hundred, maybe two, is all."

"Cheap bastard, and where is my ring? You forget you have a wife already?"

"Open your legs Debbie and let me see I got one."

"Tomorrow the ring, right? Come on over."

I pour a whisky, light a cigarette and lean back against the bed headboard. Both she and the scotch taste the same as always and I ain't complaining.

"How did you get here? I didn't see a car."

"Shit. The last I saw of it, it was sailing down Rodeo Road. Greg's going to go ape shit when he finds out." She rolls over laughing; it is apparent that it is, or was, his car. "Which reminds me John. The shit is going to come down heavy on you if the boys know you are back in town. I am serious John, if they knew, they would look and find you."

"We won't be here but a couple of days, we'll be OK."

"Don't play the tough gringo here Johnny. This is not tea-bag land. Here they will cut your throat. You better believe it."

Her forefinger flashes across her throat. The expression on her face makes me believe even she is as capable.

"I believe it."

"What time you got?"

"A little after six."

"Really! I got to split. Greg will have a search party out by now. What are you doing tonight?"

"Thought I would take a walk over to Rodeo Nites. I'll be in there around nine, do you think you can make it?"

"Sure."

"Watch you're not followed Debbie."

"Do not worry. *Hasta la vista* Johnny, you be a good boy."

She exits in half dry clothing, light cotton slacks clinging to her small frame; she looks good.

The bulk of my clothes remain packed in the cases. The rest are hung in the closet, not too many because I don't intend to be hanging around too long. One-hundred dollar bills are neatly folded then slotted into a nylon Velcro wallet. The wallet is pushed deep into my right trouser pocket. In all my life, I never lost a penny. Always the right leg pocket. The snub nose is primed with five hollow point rounds and laid to rest under the pillow. Hollow points have soft noses; the tips are dished so as to splay open on impact. Even with the low velocity of such a hand gun as this, these bullets will blow a face apart.

Planning for the future? I am now seven hundred and fifty miles east of Las Vegas. I don't see any heat coming from that quarter for at least a week, maybe two. Leaving the pick-up was a smart move. Do Angel's people still think I'm doing walkabouts in Vegas? It would take ages to check all the casinos, if that was at all possible. Then there is Debbie. What on earth brings me here to Santa Fe when I know it could be dangerous to my health and I could be traced to this city through the Clark County computer? She is a pain in the arse but she is street smart and I may be in need of her native tongue when we get on our travels. Her Spanish is fluent and as a road mate she will be better than most men: blow jobs and . . .

Out of the shower and the loudest noise I'm hearing is my stomach. Apart from the burger I ain't been eating too good in the last few days, but that is not surprising in the circumstances. Famished, I have the perfect restaurant in mind to put things to rights. Tortilla Flats, not two blocks away, is one of the best Ma and Pa Mexican restaurants in town. The more I think about the house special, the faster I get dressed.

The house special is chilli *rellenos*. The dish contains two large poblano chillies, each seven or eight inches long, stuffed with cheese and onions then fried in batter.

"How would you like your chilli sir, red or green?"

"Which is the hottest?"

"Green."

Like the old *vindaloo* it gets the old trumper in one hell of a state. I'll be farting up Debbie's back all night long. Lucky girl.

The meal was delicious, topped off with pecan pie. A decent tip is left and I make my way against on-coming traffic along Cerrillos Road. There are no sidewalks so I pick my way in the darkness. The rains have long gone and the ground has hardened up again. The ground is stony and difficult to negotiate. Luckily, Rodeo Nites is only a couple of blocks south. Seeing her outline against the sky, I tread gingerly down the slope to her inviting doors.

Although it's only eight thirty, the parking lot is near to full; this is a popular venue. But today, a Sunday, the band must be of some note to draw such a crowd. Four dollars gains me entrance then it's a long walk to the bar, situated at the far end of the dance floor. At the bar I position myself so I can observe the main entrance as Debbie will not enter without an escort. A can of Bud Light is soon within my reach and with my back to the bar I can observe both the dance floor and the entrance.

The floor show is something else, everyone is dressed in boots to bandannas. This is real skiptamaloo country. The performers are mostly Hispanic, which is about right for this neck of the woods. Anglo and Indians make the rest of the party. But the the real show is on the floor. Can these people dance! I have been in this place dozen of times and it still grabs me. These cowboys and cowgirls glide across the timber in style. I have never seen anything like it, though I confess my knowledge of dancing is somewhat limited. I have tried my hand in here before with a senorita to the tune of a two-step and I didn't get away with it then.

There must be six hundred people here tonight. To this crowd I must look like a Wall Street bond dealer – dark grey trousers and Austin Reed jacket. Several groups of men are hanging around the room, tightly-grouped, the worse for wear as they have been on the piss all day. I can only guess they have been to The Downs, a small race track on the outskirts of the city. My choice of clothing could have been better.

Unlike Vegas, where, once you are in the safety of a casino, trouble is something you never see (a raised voice even, and it's on yer way buddy), here tonight anything is possible. The drunken Indian, the angry Anglo, or the one I have my eyes on at present, the macho Mex. The wallet gets pushed deeper.

I spot Debbie walking alongside the cash-till close to the entrance. I motion her forward and watch as she skirts the dance floor with that slow sexy walk. Those hips gently moving side to side move a few eyes besides my own.

"I made it John." You always make it Deb.

"Any problems back home Deb?"

"No, they are all spaced out, bunch of fuckin' assholes. Tell you John, they are drivin' me crazy. Buy me the castle John?"

"Never mind. What are you drinking?"

"White wine with a little ice."

"Has Greg found his car yet?"

"Hah! You would not believe it. When the rains stopped they came looking for me. They found the car in a ditch, I would have loved to have seen their faces. It's a wreck, as though it was any fuckin' good anyway. Good riddance is what I say:"

The dancers dance.

"You got the marriage certificate at home?"

"You need it?"

"We both need it. I think we need to visit immigration down in Albuquerque, get me a temporary work permit at least."

"Have you all your paperwork John?"

"Well I'm goin' to lie through my teeth anyway."

"What's new!"

Debbie takes off to the restroom. While she is away I get strange looks from a group of Hispanics, and from one in particular sat at a table just off the bar. I don't take much notice because I don't see any connection between him and Debbie, but I got my eye on him and I smell trouble. Debbie gets back unmolested but now I'm feeling on edge, these guys are still looking over to us.

"Where do you fancy going to? You like the ocean?"

"I have never seen the ocean. I would love to walk on a beach and feel the waves against my legs." I can imagine. "Let's go to the sea John. I will make you a happy man I promise."

I turn to attract the bartender's attention. One of the Hispanics moves off the table to draw alongside me. I don't get it. He has to talk across me to talk to Debbie yet there is room besides her. I straight away don't like the look of this character. He is jabbering away in Spanish to

Debbie. Her eyes flick nervously at him and then me for reassurance. She answers back in Spanish. The reply is full of words I don't understand, but I get the drift. It appears he doesn't, because he doesn't look too pleased and moves swiftly back to his mates. I watch him all the way back to the table. This bastard I like even less now and I know the possible outcome.

"You OK Debbie? You know this scumbag?" She shakes her head.

"No. Take no notice John. They have been at the race track all afternoon and are drunk. Forget it."

His friends smile and make wisecracks. They have sly narrow eyes, wet with drink. Their faces are round and sweaty. I don't like the feel of this one bit!

I would love to forget it but this twat's giving me looks that could kill. Fuck me! He's on his feet and making his way over. Has this guy got a problem? My adrenaline is starting to pump. I'm weighing him up as he makes his way, five seven and stocky, small hands that are unusual on such a frame.

I'm still hoping he will fuck off, but no chance. He starts jabbering again at Debbie then turns to me. I have my back firmly against the bar.

"You English. *Que no?*"

He is being very confident; he has plenty of

his countrymen at the bar and I guess he thinks I'm outgunned. Which I am.

"I'm English."

"Santa Fe a small place. *Si?*"

I brace myself against the bar.

"Take a walk pal, you're out of order!" The tone of my voice backs him off. Debbie starts to speak but I don't take my eyes off him.

"Be careful John, he's losing face with his . . . Johnny Johnny!"

I slightly turn my head and arch my back over the brass rail, his fist is swinging towards me. From past experiences I know that all that goes before me now will be acted out in slow motion, as if watching as a spectator, cool and controlled. His fist glances high on my cheek-bone, leaving his face fully exposed. It doesn't come any better than this. My forehead crashes into his face. Blood from the gash on his nose hits and smarts my eye. He starts to fall, clutching at my clothing, pulling me down on top of him. I got slightly unbalanced after the head butt but it don't matter now, blows are raining into his face.

The expected hands start to pull and drag me off him, our legs tangle as they begin to pull us apart. My luck is still in as the bouncers finally separate us. He leaves his legs wide open. My foot boots squarely into his bollocks and he rolls on to his side as he is dragged away from me. I get a fleeting glance at Debbie. She appears in shock, hands pressed to her face.

The bouncers run me out of the main door, bolting it behind them. No other person is allowed out behind us. After the heat of battle the cool night air is refreshing, but I am boiling inside. I cannot see the Mex, so I guess they hustled him out of the side door. The bouncers are getting light entertainment listening to my heated vocabulary with its English accent.

"Bring the bastard here, I'll kill him!"

"You alright?" One of the bouncers moves in front of me.

"I look alright, don't I?"

The smallest of them walks to the corner of the building.

"He'll be coming around that corner any moment – do yourself and everybody here a favour, take it easy."

The Mex comes round the corner and a sorry sight he looks. I have done a good number on him but I still want some more. After all, he started this, took the surprise initiative and blew it. He comes closer and I see better the damage that has been inflicted, his face is cut in several places soaking his white shirt to crimson.

"Who started the trouble?" shouts one of the bouncers.

The bartender who served my first and only drink steps forward.

"I seen it all Allen. The Englishman's OK."

Allen looks me over, a smile breaking on his big ugly face.

"You brought a gal with you. Right?"

"Yeah, she's still inside."

"Right! You go back inside."

"What about his friends?"

"They won't touch you I promise. Go back inside before I change my mind."

Mex offers his hand. Turning square on, I push my full body weight into him. Unprepared, he spins into the bouncers' arms. My body is still shaking with anger and it doesn't go unnoticed.

"Cool it down bro', you're doin' alright. Just walk back in an' everything will be just dandy." I get the message.

I make my way back to the main entrance in the company of the bouncers. I don't look back but I hear Allen giving my adversary a right bollocking and telling him not to return for at least one month.

Debbie is still standing at the bar. The bartenders must have told her I would be coming back in because she doesn't look too surprised to see me.

"Sorry about that Deb." I am sorry she had to see the violence.

"No matter John, no matter. Are you alright?"

"A drink is what I need. Shout it up for me while I go for a piss." I need to check the plumbing for other reasons, to see if any of Pedro's friends are going to cause any trouble. It would be prudent to know now instead of later, when the drink has been flowing. I remember the faces from his table and none of them follow me into the restroom.

The drinks are on the house. One of the bouncers came over and told the bartender to serve up gratis for the rest of the evening. Why? My only guess is that this isn't the first time Pedro has caused trouble. Perhaps it's the first time someone has given him a bloody nose. I do know we won't be stopping to take great advantage of the offer. I might be flavour of the month at this moment, but things could change for the worst later on. There will be other troubles to come and mine will be quickly forgotten, leaving me vulnerable.

"It's early hours yet Deb, fancy taking a cab downtown and eating at the La Fonda. Romantic and expensive. What do you say?"

"I say get serious and look at yourself in the mirror. Go to the restroom now. You have been in a fight and it shows. There is no chance of going downtown."

"I've been the restroom already."

"Go look at yourself again if you don't believe me."

"Tell me what you want to do then?"

"Why don't you buy some liquor at Remon's lounge bar then we can grab a burger on the way to the motel. All inside two blocks. Come on John, let's get the fuck out of here."

All this time my eyes have been all over the bar and especially the table area where the friends are seated. The only telephones are in the lobby and these I can see from where I have positioned myself at the bar. None of his friends have been into the lobby. This could be the best time to move, before they drink too much or use a telephone.

Back in the Thunderbird Inn we unwrap our shopping: chilli burgers and French fries, one bottle of lemonade and a pint of Chivas. My cheekbone is getting a little sore and checking in the mirror I see it's swelling slightly. Debbie ain't a drinker and waters her whisky disgracefully; mine comes straight up. Normally, Chivas and I don't like company, when we get high together she gets jealous, then the third party may try to break us up and soon there is aggro. Tonight I'll mix her with lemonade.

"How long have we got Deb?" She is stretched out on the queen size.

"That depends on where we go from here? Why shouldn't I go back to Greg tonight?"

"What do you mean?"

"I have plenty to lose going along with you. A good job and somewhere to live. OK, I have to room with a load of jerks, but what have you to offer me?"

I have tried all night to keep Greg and his

cronies out of all conversation. But after all my past troubles with that cunt his name was bound to crop up in the long course of the evening.

"That's exactly it isn't it? Do you honestly think those guys give two fucks what happens to you? It's a joke. Tell me how many times you have to find the rent money? Ha, better still, tell me how many times they dip into their pockets for groceries or anything else for that matter?"

"At least I have a bed to sleep in. Am I going to be sleeping in the back of an old Dodge in the middle of some goddamn desert? What are we going to do for money?"

"I have a few grand."

"The car is going to cost that amount?"

The third whisky hits my lips. I dare not tell her the amount of cash I have. She would have spent it all before the fourth glass.

"Can I trust you John? It's no good looking at me like that. I know you, fuck face. Just you promise me that you will never leave me in some out of the way place. At least get me back here, promise?"

"I'm here now ain't I? I promised you Sunday and here I am. Don't worry about a thing."

"Don't worry about a thing! That's rich coming from you. Where did you learn to fight like that? An English prison?"

"No one teaches you how to fight. It's

instinctive like sex. You of all people should know that Debbie."

"So, that scar. What is the story?"

She moves closer.

I shake my head.

"You have all the answers wise guy. You will need to fight more than one drunken *hombre* if the boys visit. They still talk about you and they hate you. Till then, come to bed and play with me, bring the bottle with you." This is it with Debbie. There is never a clear pattern in her behaviour. Blowing hot and cold, one minute exploding like a bottle of pop, the next an invitation to make love. Maybe the uncertainty is what excites me? Always sailing in uncharted waters, bobbing and rolling in her ever present wildness.

Yeah, Greg and his hombres I don't wish to see. In general I am in good shape: out of Vegas in one piece, untraceable bank notes tucked away in a safe and a bottle of ten year malt in my hand and what's lying besides me don't smell and taste too bad either.

"Open 'em up Deb, I'm a coming in!"

The brilliant early morning sunlight crashes my sleep; the sun penetrating all corners of the room. My half-closed eyes scan the room. The watch-face tells me it's eight thirty. I rest the watch on top of the bedside cabinet. It clinks against the butt of the Rossi.

I place the gun in the drawer – Debbie gets nervous around shooters and after last night's fiasco she would be specially so.

The half-empty bottle stands within arms' reach on the floor. Did we drink so much? I pinch my forehead: the pain. My kingdom for an aspirin and a cup of rosie! I roll out of the pit and head for the shower. The tepid water brings me back to some sort of life. Stepping out, I hear Debbie stirring.

"What time do you have?"

"Close on nine."

"Shit! I have to call my office."

The old teeth are getting the full Monty this morning but still my mouth feels akin to a gorilla's armpit.

"Where you going John?"

"To grab a couple of cokes – there's a machine at the end of the veranda." Outside I stretch my limbs and fill my lungs with the thin clean air. It's a beautiful morning. In the cool shade I look at the flawless blue sky, not a cloud to be seen, a canvas of flat blue, that blue known only to the desert. The Coke helps wash away some debris. Debbie waves aside my offer of Coke. She is busying her teeth with my brush.

"I want you to stay here a while Deb. I need to borrow one of Jeff's motors. We can then spend the morning checking the car lots."

"Don't be talking all day or I just might not be here when you get back. Got it!"

"Back in the shake of a donkey's dick."

I will be. I don't want Debbie doing walkabouts on me. Greg and friends will be doing the grand tour anytime now.

To cross the six lane highway on Cerrillos takes some skill. Crossing at the lights two blocks away will make the walk into a hike. I wait for a break in the traffic and for fleeting seconds make Olympic Gold. Once over it's only ten minutes to Jeff's office. The sun is beating down unmercifully and thankfully it's all downhill.

The office door is wedged ajar and as I approach the doorway I see Jeff's secretary, Maxine, pecking away at a computer keyboard.

"Hey John! Where have you been? And why have you not called all this time? People ask after you, so in future you keep in touch. Do you hear me?" Maxine leans back in her chair and offers me her outstretched hand. The hand is delicate, fine-boned and dark brown, showing a greater mix of Indian blood to Spanish.

Maxine is on the thirty mark, skinny and pretty. The day-creche takes care of the kids while she works her five-twenty an hour. She pays the rent, runs a tidy motor and survives her corner. Max and I have mutual respect. She knows in general I'm a cheeky bastard, but I never chased her tail.

"Good to see you too Max. Thank goodness someone is worrying about me. You're still looking your beautiful self. How are the kids?"

"The kids are fine. Rosie's in the fifth grade now and the other is bullshit," she laughs. "Hey! Congratulations. Debbie stopped by, did Jeff tell you? Now she will stop your gallop you'll see."

"I hope not Max. Have you seen Jeff this morning? I need some wheels."

"*Some wheels*. Hey! English talk. He is out on business and will not be back before two. He has left the keys to the Mazda pick-up. He said it's low on gas. Going to be in town long John?"

"Not too long Max. A couple of days maybe."

"Do not dare leave this town without taking me out to lunch, do you hear me? Let me pour coffee – it's a fresh pot."

Sipping the coffee I take a walk through to the workshop at the back of the building. Threading my way through the used restaurant equipment I see stoves and deep fryers that I serviced months before. They should be long gone by now.

"Has he replaced me yet Max?"

"No. You will have to come back and settle with Debbie. Anyway it's been too quiet around here without you."

The coffee is black and strong. We make small talk. She denies any boyfriends, some things never change. There is talk of restaurants that have flourished, have folded, have scammed, and those that now serve the finest chicken *fajitas*. Max is good company but I cannot allow myself to settle.

"Look Max, I have to run, I'll be back around three. Take care."

"Don't forget the lunch John. Tomasita's. You owe me!"

"I owe you Max."

Back at the Thunderbird, Debbie occupies herself with the remote, switching constantly between channels and driving me doolally. Sharp words and five minutes later we are turning out of the parking lot. This is an easy city to drive; the roads are wide and the place is small. Used car lots are everywhere. Cerrillos and St. Michael's Drive it seems hold most of the dealers. As low as five hundred can get wheels spinning. We cruise the lots. I'm not too keen to use a dealer for reasons of later identification.

We pull off Rodeo Road on to the parking lot of a large shopping Mall.

"Selling cars in Dillards now, are they?" This is a massive shopping Mall. The parking lot has hundreds of cars parked up; maybe I will find the one I want here. Debbie's giving me looks like I lost my marbles. We slowly cruise the lanes of parked cars, dozens have 'for sale' stickers in the rear windows.

I am waiting for the obvious from Debbie.

"Tell me clever fucker, when you find the one you want, are we going to sit here all day and wait for the owner to show up?"

I spot a vehicle.

"Debbie, I'm going to drop you at the main door. Buy two coffees and anything else you need. I will meet you in fifteen minutes. OK?"

"But . . ."

"Do this for me Debbie, please. Never mind the buts."

Off she goes, pulling her tongue out on the way. Boy, I bet she was some difficult child. I move on and soon I pull the pick-up alongside an old Buick. A sale sign takes half the rear window. She's long, clean and green. Looking around the car I see it's as clean in as out. No rust, well it's desert so I don't really expect any. The windows are tinted dark but I can see it's an automatic. All in all this has been a real motor car in its day. I am checking the white walled tyres . . . I begin to jot down the telephone number on the rear screen.

"Can I help young man?"

"Yes ma'am, I was admiring your Buick."

Buick means something. The word car would never get the response I need.

"That's very nice sir, an' it's nice to hear your accent. I visit over the pond every year an' how does you folk manage, that's what I want to know?"

It's hard to guess her age – sixty-five, maybe

older I don't know. I do know that she seems to be a nice old lady. Never mind the pleasantries though, it's the car I'm after and I ask the price.

"Twelve hundred dollars is the asking figure young man."

"Can you tell me her history, ma'am?"

"My husband bought this car. Brand spanking new in seventy four. He was an Air Force Colonel down in Tucson. He died five years ago, bless his soul. This old gal has been in the desert all her life and I guess that's the reason she's in such good shape."

"Has she been regularly serviced?"

"The Air Force did all the service work, regular as clockwork every two thousand miles. Now I have the oil changed every three. I'm getting too old for all this drivin'."

"Is twelve the best you can do?"

"Take her round the lot. If you like her I'll settle on a thousand." She opens the passenger door and waves me to the driver's side. I move round and take the wheel.

"My wife is in the Mall. She will be out any second. Would you mind waiting?"

"Sit in the car young man – it's hot out there. I'll turn on the air conditioning. Married are you? Did you bring you wife with you from England?"

"No, I married her out here. Vegas in fact."

"How exciting! You will find American

women different. Women of today are far too aggressive."

Tell me.

"Hey Deb, over here."

Man! If she walked any slower she would fall over. My impatience shows and a smile breaks on the old lady's face.

"You take the pick-up Debbie and follow us on to Airport Road."

She moves closer to the Buick and leans into the window waiting for me to hand her the keys to the Mazda.

"Is this it?" She has a face like an undertaker's clerk as she jumps into the pick-up. Her red Cadillac has turned into a green Buick. Life sucks hey Debbie!

"Just follow us! I need to drop the lady off and pick up the paperwork," I call across.

Forget the Cadillac, this baby drives like a dream. The engine purrs as we exit on to Rodeo: power steering, light as any Jag I've driven. This car in its day would have been the bee's knees. In the rear view mirror I see Debbie, her long face bites into a stick of gum then, seeing my eyes, her tongue pokes out. The old lady still wears half a smile as I concentrate on the road ahead.

"Make the next right young man."

We turn off Airport Road on to a trailer park. The old dear lives in a double wide trailer about three hundred yards inside the main gate. I now have a chance to give the Buick a good going over, though I've already made my mind up. This car is what I'm looking for. Its large engine and water jacket will easily get me along hot desert highways. The large engine block is oil-free and hardly breathing. I don't have to look any further.

Money and documents change hands.

"Take the wheel Deb. I'll follow you in the pick-up, yes, back to Jeff's office."

"How's she drive Debs?"

"I like it but . . ."

"Hey you guys, what's goin' down? You just bought it John?"

"I have Jeff, an' I think I got myself a real workhorse."

"You certainly got that John. But you ain't goin' far on a tank of gas, you do know that?"

"What's money Jeff," says Debbie as she steps inside the office to talk with Max. Jeff walks slowly around the car, nodding his head in approval.

"You will be travelling in style John. When are you thinking of going?"

"Tonight. I will pick the money up last thing, if that's alright with you. Debbie has not a clue as to what has happened. I don't know Jeff, should I leave her here? Is she going to be a problem?"

"She will be OK, you'll see. Tell me, did

Debbie give her Santa Fe address when you married in Vegas?"

"Yeah, and I know what you are going to say. A great mistake I made, but how the fuck do I explain that she needs to be a resident of Kathmandu on her wedding day!"

"You're darn right about the mistake; they will come straight here looking for you. Both your names on the marriage certificate an' all. Look John! I don't wish to know which direction you are heading, but do me the favour of calling me every evening at six o'clock. Six, remember."

"I'll remember you're making me nervous."

"You should be nervous, you crazy bastard." He shakes his head incredulously. "I don't know about you John? Let's go inside for coffee."

Inside the office, Max is busy pouring coffee.

"I have talked with Debbie. You have made her happy John." She places her hand on my arm. "Remember the lunch you promised me? Don't forget now."

"I won't forget."

"Don't forget the time John, six o'clock. Right?" Jeff and I leave the office's air conditioning and stand at the rear of the Buick.

"You'll be in the office at six? Working late?"

"I'll be here at six all week. I have a lot of catching up to do. You know, State and Federal taxes. Then how would you know?"

"Hey! Maybe one day I'll get around to such mundane happenings." This don't sit too well.

"You bet! I take it you ain't seen nothing of Debbie's crowd yet?"

"Not yet and I don't want to. Maybe I should take off right now, leave her and those crazy bastards to it. That would be the way, wouldn't it?"

Jeff nods. "That would be the way to go. Listen John, you go easy and don't forget to call me."

We ease the Buick off Ruffina on to Cerrillos. Everything tells me it's got to be tonight. Now I need dust between myself and Santa Fe.

"Right Deb, now we need an insurance broker. You have your licence? OK, let's do that, then transfer the car over to you."

"But John . . ."

"Cut the shit Debbie, are you coming along or not?"

"The money worries me John. What on earth are we going to do when we get to California?"

"Don't worry about money, we have plenty."

"Show me!"

I count out five hundred bucks and hand them over. A smile crosses her face.

"When you've done with the insurance, go buy yourself some light clothing."

"Six hundred John, make it six."

Back in the Thunderbird the night is beginning to wrap its blanket around us. Debbie has catwalked her new clothing and is now preoccupied reading a women's magazine while I stalk the air conditioning machine as it rattles along. The obvious thing would be to turn it off but Debbie insists on it freezing my bollocks off. My attention is distracted by the noise, but Debbie's is not. I miss the slamming of the car door; Debbie doesn't.

"Fuck! It's Greg."

"You're jokin!" Shit! Rolling off the bed I snatch up the .38 and race, naked, to the right hand side of the door. No sooner am I there when there is a hammering at the door. He cannot know I am in the room.

"Bitch! Open the fuckin' door. Now!"

I whisper to Debbie that he knows my old truck, this new car must be throwing him.

"Open up."

Panic is written all over her face. I motion for her to slip the lock and move well back. The lock slips, the door bangs open and sure enough he's running for her. She looks desperately towards me. In that split second he stops and turns, sensing now there is a third person in the room. It throws him off balance and he stumbles against the bed, spinning to the floor.

"Shut the fuckin' door Debbie." Debbie is frozen to the spot.

"Lock the door! *Now* Debbie, move it!"

I walk slowly towards Greg, slightly crouched with the pistol pointing at his head all the time.

"Now move over to the bed Debbie, that's it, where I can see you. That's it. Don't move a fucking inch, hear me?" She nods her head. The colour drained from her face.

Greg has attempted to stand. The closeness of the .38 has changed his mind, a new smell suggests he is in need of a change of underpants.

"I see your manners are still as poor as shit. Move an' I'll blow your bastard brains out."

"We will get you, English bastard. You will never leave . . ."

The barrel breaks through his front teeth. A lucky blow, as his head wobbles beneath me. Gotcha! The force of the thrust shatters and tears his mouth apart, even with the barrel stuck deep in his mouth, his screams overshadow the clanking of the cooling system. Grabbing his hair and slamming his head to the floor I look up at Debbie. She is standing holding her hands to her face. She looks in shock. Blood is gushing over my hands and on to the floor. You're gonna need a good dentist buddy.

"Get your things together. Now Debbie, now!"

She starts to move in disorganised circles, her eyes showing fear, fear of me. Twice in twenty-four hours Debbie has seen violence, my violence. In self defence maybe, but this is a side of me that Debbie has not seen before. It's made worse by the speed and severity of this attack on Greg.

"Move it! For fucks sake Debbie, all your gear. Just throw it into cases." From slow to full speed she begins to stuff the cases. Our things are mixed in the haste to pack.

"Leave the holdall. On second thoughts leave everything by the door. Hey! Are you listening to me?" Her face is gripped with fear.

"Get in the car. The keys are in that drawer. Please Debbie move it. I ain't goin' to tell you again!"

She starts to bundle her small amount of things together and moves quickly out of the door.

"Turn the engine over and warm her. I need to clean up here."

Only minutes have passed since Greg burst through the door. A lot has happened in that short time. Greg is one hell of a mess, so is the room. Blood is splashed over the walls and on the carpet. There must have been one hell of a racket as Greg was getting his face re-arranged but no one has come to see what all the noise was about. There is no time for cleaning duties. I needed Debbie out of the room while I gave Greg my going-away present: the pistol whips about his head.

"Don't fuck with me again you bastard." He doesn't hear me. I leave him lying in his blood and lock the door.

Moving quickly to the window, I see Debbie

sitting motionless in the passenger side of the car. Right! I gotta move it. The television's sound is turned up. This, I hope, will say all's well down at room 6b. Naked, I hit the shower; motel soap washes the blood from my arms and legs. Quickly I am out and bending besides my holdall. Greg lays motionless on his side. What a mess. My eyes never leave him as I climb into jeans and T-shirt. I'm still wringing wet. Shoes and socks I give a miss to. I'll find time for such dress sense between here and where to.

Debbie is silent on the drive to Jeff's office. She doesn't look in my direction once. Just as I foot the brake outside the office, she turns sharply to face me.

"A bad dream is what it is! A bad fucking dream. Get real John, there was no need for that shit back there."

"Bollocks. I owed him one from the last time. Right?"

"You're wrong John. You better get your ass moving. What are we doing here?"

"Wait here, I'll explain later."

The ignition key goes in my pocket; I do not want Debbie doing a runner with the motor – just a little precaution. The Greyhound bus company has no appeal at this hour.

"What are you doing with the office keys? Does Jeff know you have them?"

The safe opens sweetly. I peel off ten one

hundred dollar bills, then put them back inside the
safe. Thanks Jeff.

"I guess we need to make some space
between us and Santa Fe. Shall we drive south,
head for El Paso?"

"I don't give a monkey's fuck John. Just
go."

"Turn the radio on Deb. See if she works."

"Turn it on yourself big shot. You and me
are going to do some serious talkin'. You hear?"

Arlo Guthrie rocks us out of the city limits
on to Highway Twenty. That old song is the only
thing that breaks the silence.

> *Good-night America how are ya?*
> *Say don't you know me I'm your*
> *favourite son.*
> *I'm the train they call The City Of New*
> *Orleans.*
> *I'll be gone five hundred miles when the*
> *day is done.*

Debbie lies on her side with her knees tucked up. Her head rests on my lap. She is on the edge of sleep. I curl her long soft hair between my fingers. She doesn't respond.

The Buick responds well to the open road, gliding effortlessly into the night. On the horizon in the distance an arc of light appears. We are approaching Albuquerque. The traffic will be light at this time of night but passing through the city I will stay in central lanes so as not to be thrown off my destination route. It will take ten minutes to pass through and clear the city. I will then feel a little safer and look for a roadside motel.

"Wake up Deb, I think we got us a bed."

"Where are we?"

"Just south of Belem. Come on Deb, I want you to do the talking. This English accent is a dead giveaway."

She talks us in. The accommodation is a small truck-stop, maybe twenty rooms with an office attached to a diner out front. Twenty-six bucks and "make yourselves at home folks". We decline the early morning call. Cases are opened and spilled in silence. I feel drained from the excitements and excursions of the past twenty-four hours. Man! What a blast. A little remorse sets in. You were right Deb. There was no need for such severity. What's done is done though. I cannot turn the clock back. Here's the rub: tomorrow it will be as if nothing had happened. I'll shake my head: a bad dream. Like, I don't see Angel no more, just the money. Tomorrow I'll shake my head an' all I'll see is Debbie, and Greg will be gone forever.

"So tell me? Where are we running to? You have plans? Am I included? Yes or no? You sure as fuck got more trouble than this whole State could shake a stick at."

"Plans? California ain't it?"

"California! You mother fucker! You say it just like that. What you did back there was disgusting. You hear me?"

"Keep your voice down. You're gonna be waking the building."

Her Latino blood is coming to the boil. Pacing the floor, her small quick steps are exaggerated by rapid arm movements. She moves along the bedside. I prop myself on to my elbow and wait for the verbals to die and the physicals to start. Here it comes. Whack . . . whack . . . I make a half-hearted attempt to defend myself. Small tight fists pound into my body as I shield my face. Come on Debbie, let it go. For her size, she is surprisingly strong. The blows don't hurt a bit, but then they shouldn't. It's over, she slumps on to the end of the bed and sobs her heart out. Her hands tighten on her knees, knuckles pinched white. Tears flow and stain her pink blouse.

Resting my head back on the raised pillow I light a cigarette and look hard at Debbie. Even in distress, she looks proud and handsome.

Some tough twenty two years she has led – I've heard the story. Forget idyllic conceptions about the Latino family: poor as church mice but nevertheless keeping the unit together; children at play at siesta time; papa swinging gently in the hammock, singing; baby Juan sleeping peacefully, clutching at his father's breast. It's mostly a load of old bollocks. In most cases, the kids, especially if they're girls, are farmed out to their grandparents at an early age, as was Debbie. Grandpa dies, grandma gets old and sick and the girl gets dumped on to older brothers or sisters. These are possibly married. Entering puberty the girl has to take any shit that comes down from cousin J.J. At sixteen she's on her own; her education has suffered along with, in some cases, her body.

The cigarette smoke drifts lazily in the still air. Hanging loosely between my lips, smoke smarts my eyes. Slack tobacco sucks on to my lips and is playfully spat in Debbie's direction, falling short. Sitting upright I lean forward and stroke Debbie's waist. She looks over, her eyes dark and wet.

"What if anything should happen between us John. Where would I go? You once told me about burning bridges. Remember?"

"So that's it! Your main concern lays with home and hombres eh?"

"Well! You're a fucker and no mistake. It's just that . . ." Words fail her. I suppose there's a first time for everything.

"I tell you this though baby, I'd give it a month or two. Reckon Greg boy's kissin' is gonna be off the mark till then."

"Bastard!" In she comes. Wham, bam. This time the old head has to take a few shots.

The head is a little clearer this morning. On account no doubt that I left the remains of the Chivas Regal back in Santa Fe. I wander out into the light of day. Yeah got the car parked well back and out of view of the highway.

"Two coffees to go please."

Debbie is still in the land of the dead as I enter the room. The smell of the coffee and a nudge in the side wakes her. She grunts into life but I know it will take ages for her to get her arse into gear. I settle into a chair and study the State Farm road atlas. Where to after El Paso? Is it to be West? Tucson?

"It's after ten Debbie. Will we see the open road to-day?"

"Sure. Tell you what, let's take a shower together, then breakfast, then . . ." There's that change in her again, like last night's tears never happened.

"Shake it Debbie. Drop the key off at the office. I'll check the oil and water. Catch me at the pumps."

We cruise on down the highway, dropping in altitude all the time, the desert becoming sparse of vegetation. This is not spectacular canyon country but the air is sweet and clear and the sky is blue and cloudless. Every now and then to our left tall bushy green-leafed trees stand in contrast against the drab desert – in straight lines, as if marching in formation south to a known watering hole. No, these lucky trees flank the banks of the Rio Grande.

The air conditioning is turned down because Debbie is lying naked on the bench seat. One foot resting on the seat, the other on the floor. Her legs are wide apart, showing me this morning's breakfast. Her fingers stroke through coarse pubic hair and part her pink cunt lips. Man! There must be a law against this kind of activity while doing fifty-five on a public highway. Debbie has not read the rule book because soon she is on her knees and my jeans are being tugged off my slightly raised arse. One hand on the wheel and the other stroking her arse as she sucks me. Very spacious these old cars. I can believe the old story that most

Americans have their first sexual encounter in the back of a Dodge.

"Las Cruces, John. Are we going to pull over? I need to eat."

I check the time, ten minutes to six. I will need to be making a call to Jeff anyway.

"Eat the fucker this time Debbie. Every time you pick a little."

"OK dad."

"Order me the same. Whatever you are having will do. I have to make a call."

"How's it going Jeff?" There is quite a long pause.

"I'm sorry Tom. All afternoon I have been calling your office. It will be here in the morning. Yeah, Red Star. I'll bring it myself. Sorry about that. Thanks for the deposit. Have a good one."

Nice one Jeff. The pantomine means that there is an undesirable in the office. The deposit means the grand that was left in the safe.

It's got to be the law. Does it concern Angel? Or that wanker Greg? It has to be Greg.

"Calling your boyfriend huh?"

"So I'm queer."

"Yes, I could have told you that this morning! Stay away from my ass in future."

Her burnt plum is the last thing I have on my mind at this moment, believe me.

"You looked kinda apprehensive in the phone booth. Bad news?"

"Well Debbie, seeing we are down the road anyways, I think I'd better put you in the picture."

"Is it something you did to Greg?"

"No. I robbed a dope dealer back in Vegas."

"So what's the big deal. How much did you take?"

"Eighty seven grand, and that is the problem."

"Sweet Jesus! A problem? You got the fucking castle."

"It wouldn't pay the plumber. Get serious."

The waitress brings a salad starter. Debbie is all excited, creaming her knickers and spilling Ranch Dressing at the very thought of a big spend. Have I done the right thing? Can I trust Debbie? Can I fuck. She will turn me over as quick as lightning, but what can I do? The shit could come down heavy and Debbie knowing, it may give her a chance to make a move away from me.

"There could be big trouble Debbie. That's the reason I've told you."

"Forget it John, we are a million miles away. Where do you keep the money?"

"It's stuffed up my arse! Never mind about the money, what's the main course?"

"*Carne adovada*, pork chop in red chilli. You will like it. Why the call to Jeff?"

"It's obvious Deb, our names are linked

through the computer in Las Vegas. We did get married, right? You gave your home address and if they nose around they will track down my last employer."

"You were illegal so Jeff never put you through the books. Who will know?"

"Greg knows. Now the sheriff will know. All adds up don't it?"

"It don't matter John, I'm with you." With the money more likely.

"If you like, I can drop you off on El Paso airport in the morning. If not, you have to take your chances."

"I'll take my chances. Do you know, they serve a Jail House chilli." Very appropriate. The *carne adovada* is delicious.

Another day's drive. The lights of El Paso shine below us. I do not know the geography of El Paso. I don't want to be driving around a border town at this time of night. The gas pedal eases off every mile or so. I am looking out for tidy accommodation. Restaurant and bar with a room telephone so I can phone Jeff and no ifs and buts at the switch board. Tonight I feel the need to make Debbie feel special. Quality room with good facilities. A good meal with the best house wine. It's been a long day and I need this myself. Knackered out, tired eyes and aching bones and here I am, sat on more dough than I ever set my eyes on.

"This is a nice room John, a real treat."

"Only the best for you Debbie, only the best." She pulls her tongue out.

"Hey up Jeff, it's John." It's late, hours past six o'clock, so I'm phoning him at home.

"Hold on, I'll take it in the bedroom."

Debbie cracks open a beer and hands it over as I wait for Jeff to come back on the line.

"Don't tell me where you're at John, I don't want to know. Before when you called that was the FBI in the office. It's serious shit. You ready for it?"

"Do I have a choice, I mean . . ."

"They, the Vegas police, found the broad you snitched the money from dead. The body was lying in the back of your pick-up out back of the motel."

"Fuck! Wait on Jeff. I didn't have nothing to do with her death. It happened as I told you. You gotta believe me." Debbie has gone a shade whiter, her hand shielding her mouth.

"I believe you John, but tell that to the Feds. I am thirty years old this year an' these are the first I ever met. It's serious!"

"What else did they tell you?"

"They made an arrest. Some kid from New York. Didn't give a name. Anyway, he was crashed beneath your pick-up. You believe that?" I believe it. So Jimmy never made it to San Francisco.

"What happened with him? Do you know?"

"They held him a couple of days then let him go. Fucking serious is all I know and it's you they are after." Serious it is. I left Vegas early Sunday morning. It is only Wednesday evening and already the cops are closing me down.

"They told me all there is to know about the woman, which was strange. You said she came out of Reno?"

"Yes."

"Wrong. San Francisco. A different State buddy."

"What else?"

"Her surname is Jalisco. This is the frightener – she was married to a Mex, a real one from old Mexico. Down in Guadalajara, you ever heard of it?"

"No, can't say I have."

"Drugs John. Big like General Motors. You get the picture?"

"What the fuck would they want to tell you all that shit for?"

"That's the eighty seven thousand dollar question, ain't it?"

"They know you've been here, perhaps they are passing on some kind of warning."

"Like what?"

"I can't put a finger on it, John. You still got Debbie with you?"

"No."

"Good. Thanks for the money John. Do me a favour will you?"

"Before you hang up, have the local boys been around? You know, the sheriff."

"No, should he be?"

"What's the favour Jeff?"

"Don't call me no more. Go easy now, I gotta run."

Jesus! It cannot get any worse, can it? You don't need to know where I'm at Jeff, I'm on queer street! No mistake. Don't look at me that way Debbie. I have the FBI coming from one direction and a bunch of wild Mexican dope heads coming from another. Gotta be thinking my chances of staying alive rests with the Feds. Still, at this time I'm still in front, by at least twenty-four hours, but all the Feds have to do is telephone every truck stop and motel three directions out off Santa Fe and eventually my accent is going to give the game away. I've got to get rid of Debbie. This whole deal can turn nasty at any moment and she will only be a hindrance.

Debbie throws me that what the fuck is really going on look.

"Tell me what's happening?"

"Jeff's had a visit from the police. I think it's a bust over the motel deal?" She rounds on me, her face pressed to mine.

"Lying motherfucker! I heard you on about that woman in Vegas. Dead? I heard the word!"

"There has been a problem, back in Vegas. Sometime after I left the girl got killed." I only wish I could talk to Wayne. He would know the story. But that's never going to happen. Talking with Wayne would be talking with Vegas.

"People get killed every day of the week in Vegas. It wasn't down to me." One time, at a busy road intersection in Vegas, I see the body of a naked woman lying stone dead. Spread face down on a piss-stained mattress just off the highway. The traffic barely slows. This murder ain't so different, except it's me that's in the frame.

"Don't worry then John. We are a long way from all that now." Debbie accepts Angel's death a little too easily. This is typical of her mood swings. Her change of emotion I can usually handle. But now I'm worried. Fuck, Debbie, if only you knew the severity of the situation. I have seen danger many times, from the jungles of East Asia to the scrub bush of central Africa. Where did you think I learnt all there is to know about sidearms, some factory shopfloor? Of course I was younger then, and without the added burden and distraction of someone like yourself. Fist fighting is one thing, guns another. For the first time in my life I'm starting to have doubts about my ability to cope once the shit hits the fan. Is the bottle still there? There ain't no turning back now.

Down in the bar corner, a negro plays the piano.

His fat fingers roll along the keys. I should know that tune, but it ain't coming to me.

"Same for the lady, make mine a double this time."

"Gonna get you a flight first thing in the morning. It's for the best and you have only missed three working days, so your job will still be there. I will give you enough money to set yourself up in a nice apartment. It's for the best, you'll see."

"And that's fucking it, is it? See you later Debbie. Catch you later Debbie. No chance, you hearing me?

"I'm hearing."

"Do you honestly think Greg will have any of that? Give me a break! We have been through this already."

"I don't know Debbie . . ."

"Please John, I'm begging you."

"Listen to me Debbie, and listen good. I got enough problems so no more bitchin'. You hear me?"

"I hear you John. I promise."

"OK then, it's an early call then west for Tucson."

"Arizona! You know someone?"

"Yeah. A fella I met up with last year. He's alright. We can rest up for a few days and let the heat cool."

"That's fine with me."

"Right then, let's make a wake-up call then hit the sack."

I did not sleep too good, so Debbie takes the wheel out on Highway Ten. The road atlas tells me it's gonna be Deming for breakfast. Daylight should soon be breaking behind us.

The same question keeps spinning through my mind. Why the fuck did the FBI give Jeff the deal on Angel? Do police routinely give all their information away? Do they fuck! Something is wrong. What? What if, through Jeff, the FBI are trying to get a message to me? A warning even. We pull over. Another Mexican breakfast and they will smell me coming. This chilli is starting to go through me faster than a Porsche!

"Bacon, hashbrowns and eggs over easy luv. Did I get all that the right way round?"

"You better call your friend in Tucson, John, or maybe you want to surprise him?"

"He has no telephone."

"No telephone! Everyone has a telephone!"

Richard sure don't. No kitchen or inside toilet either. Just a two-roomed adobe, an old beat-up truck and a dog called Ben. You'll love it Debbie.

"Will I like him?"

"Sure you will. He's an old Vietnam vet. Laid back an' all that jazz."

The closer we get to Tuscon, the better I am feeling. The Buick's driving like a dream – does she know she's close to home? Just inside the city limits we pull into a drive-through Dairy Queen.

"We need this John?"

"Better be eating now Deb. I ain't bankin' on Rick holdin' a full larder."

"Larder?"

We join the queue, there has to be eight or nine vehicles in front of us. Slowly we close down. Cars and trucks begin to back up behind us. Soon we reach a yellow post. On top of this at cab height is a voice box. A voice comes crackling over. "Your order please."

I should know better. I've done this before, but it's too late now.

"Double cheese burgers, large fries and medium Cokes twice please." More crackling then silence.

"Would you please speak clearer sir. I cannot understand you."

"Double cheese burgers, fries and . . ."

"Sorry sir . . ." Debbie laughs out loud. I have a problem here. The thing is this, the post cannot be but thirty feet from the deep fryer. We have a communication problem; the stupid box ain't helping and I'm close enough to shout the fucking order.

Speaking slowly don't help none. Debbie's laughing like crazy and I'm about to go bananas.

"Help me out Deb. You shout into this contraption will you?"

"Keep trying John. They love your accent is all." If that's the case, they're the only ones, because behind me now I have vehicles backing up on to the roadway. Horns are blasting and the inside of the car is getting hotter.

"Fuck this!" I slam the car door behind me. Between horn blasts, I hear abuse. All the drive-through staff are now at the window, watching anxiously as I stride towards them.

Their faces have surprise written all over them. Who is this guy? What planet has he stepped off? Young faces in their silly hats move away from the glass.

"Hey pal! Two cheese burgers, large fries and medium Cokes. Make it twice. To go! Now!"

The original server looks about him for support. A young Hispanic girl gets the drift and starts to prepare my order. We are in business, thank the Lord. The hooting and abuse has stopped. Why? Whoosh, the Buick bears down on me. Shit! It's tyres screech along the high kerbstones bordering the narrow traffic lane. Jumping, I grab the serving hatch window, the car brushes my legs as it speeds off the Dairy Queen. Jesus Christ! She's a lunatic.

"Get your arse back here. You hearing me?"

Man alive! Would you credit that? I'm gonna kill the bitch. The Buick makes a left on to the highway. A wild whoopee breaks across waste land. She makes a sharp left, snaking on to a competitor's parking lot. Crazy bastard! Brown bags and Cokes in hand I take off across waste land to close the distance. I'm within ten feet of the Buick when it comes to a halt. Her hand shows through the side window. The middle finger shoots upwards.

"You need a ride old man? You goin' some place?" She steps on the gas. Dust briefly breaks my view.

One brown bag is hurled after the car, falling short and spilling its contents, the double cheese gets booted in all directions.

That's it! Thirty yards away she breaks to stop again.

"Get your arse back here right now God-damn it. Fuck it Debbie! Don't you be pissin' me off no more." She slowly reverses. Mischief and glee are written all over her face.

"Climb aboard mister. That's it, sit up front an' join the white folk."

"I'll give you white folk!" A cheer goes up from the Dairy Queen queue. It seems every other bastard got the joke, bar me.

We remain stationary as she eats her burger. It is apparently mine that lies in the dust. What the hell! I light up and fan the still air. She still has that mischievous look about her. Debbie is one month short on twenty two and I'm close to forty three. I guess I'll never adjust to her youthful ways. How long before I get the hump and leave her some place? My present feelings tell me not too long. Debbie takes the wheel.

"Make for the west side. Once we are on South Mission I'll know where we're goin'."

Debbie moves through the city like she has been here all her life. Once out of the city I take over.

In five minutes we are passing a large flea market lot, a right and we are on to Roadrunner Road. Two blocks on the right, the corner lot, he is still there. Under the shade of a row of palm trees, Ben, a labrador-chow cross, is sat upright in the back of an old Dodge pick-up.

"Is this it?"

"We need this place a while Debbie, so like I told you, no hassle."

"It's getting worse John. What the . . ." My open hand is pushed close to her face.

"No more, no more. Try an' behave yourself, just this one time please."

Ben lifts his ears and barks as we enter the compound. Easy Ben. Inside the house I hear Richard calling to control the dog. His skinny frame pushes aside the broken fly-screen. It must have been on its last fastenings because it falls into the dirt. I guess the bright sunlight has impaired his sight because he jumps back inside the building.

"Hey Ricky, it's your old buddy John."

The first thing I see is the torn, straw Stetson appearing slowly from the doorway. That old hat has seen more summers than Rick.

"You English motherfucker, what the fuck are you trying to do to me?"

"How are you doin' Rick? Nice to see you again."

"You really had me shakin' man! Where's the big block?"

"I traded her. Meet the wife."

He's standing there, in straw hat and underpants.

"Sorry ma'am." He's stuck for something to say. "You ever been this way before?"

"Never have. This is the first palm tree I ever parked under." Rick's eyes flash. They tell me he likes her.

He turns and goes back inside. We give him time to make himself decent then enter the darkness of the building. It is hard to imagine what the builder had in mind when he laid his first block. The building is about twenty feet square, split into two rooms. Each room has an external door, with a doorway on the internal wall giving access between rooms. There are no windows, which in normal circumstances would be a pisser, but in this instance it keeps the rooms cool against the heat of the Arizona desert.

An old knuckle-head Harley lies in bits in the corner.

"Ben. Come here an' meet the lady."

"I see you ain't got the bike back together?"

"Soon buddy, soon. I'm waitin' on some parts an' money is as tight as a duck's ass. Still, not to worry, I got me some real company for a change. Didn't tell me you had such a pretty thing tucked away back there. A dark 'orse an' no mistake.

Within thirty minutes, day turns to night. Debbie has made friends with Ben and they are playing out back of the building. There is a fair bit of land to the property. A toilet and combined shower room stand on the corner of the lot. One can have a shower and a shit at the same time. Looks like the shower room was as far as the builder wanted to fetch the plumbing.

Rick is fanning the makeshift barbecue: two building blocks support a cast-off oven shelf. Warm Coors tallboys are produced. They fizz and spill some of their contents on opening.

"It's sure good to see you again, but what really brings you here?"

I go through the story. Making light the scam to six grand. I figure I'm a little late to be saved plus Ricky might have feedback and insight into what my future plans should be.

Rick pokes the fire then turns the burgers.

"Be hoping the Feds get to you before the dopers, man. I've been down that road too many times John. But then, you know that." The penny drops. Is this the message the Feds are trying to get across?

Debbie rounds the corner and I get the buns ready.

"I'm still on parole John. Remember?"

"You told me."

"You're good for a week. I can't afford no trouble with the Board. I've been in the can three times already, didn't think I was goin' to make the last deal, had been shootin' heroin for God knows how long, I tell you man."

The burgers are passed around. The dog has kept Debbie off my back for the past two hours. I like dogs.

"Just the weed now John, only weed." Ricky looks old for his forty-five years. The hamburger wobbles in his hand. He stares into the fire, deep in thought. He don't finish the burger. Ben moves in quickly and takes advantage of Rick's lack of appetite.

"I lost two brothers in Nam, you believe that shit. It was all downhill from there on in. Got myself wounded twice, doped both times, never felt a thing man!" I have heard this story before. Out of respect I keep my mouth closed and listen.

"Hey Ricky, how old is Ben?" Go back to sleep Debbie. Ricky doesn't look up and he doesn't answer the question.

"The Tet offensive back in sixty seven.

Khesanh, yeah baby, that was the big one. We patrolled the perimeter most nights, meeting Charlie at pre-arranged places to swap dollars for smoke. It was the Vietcong's main source of revenue. Anyway, this night Charlie don't show. It can only mean one thing. The base is about to be hit. I got hit by mortar shrapnel going back through the wire. The dog? He's nine years old, I think."

Ricky pokes the fire. His eyes still fixed to the flames. Something tells me he's still shootin' heroin.

"Sorry to hear about your brothers Rick," I tell him. Debbie is being unusually quiet.

"Yeah. Well, anyway, when I made it back, like some misplaced person, I started running weed out of old Mexico. Chihuahua, south of Juarez. That went good 'til I got bust by the border cops. El Paso never was my favourite. Anyway, next time round I raised the stakes to cocaine. Big bucks but got bust in LA." I wait a few seconds.

"Did you do much time?" He lifts his head slowly. His eyes narrow. I look across to Debbie. She has shown no reaction to his drug dealing and prison time.

"Two years, John. Then out again and I gets caught on a run through Pennsylvania. By this time I'm snortin an' shooting the shit like there's no tomorrow. So here I am, forty five and fucked beyond all reason. Another burger

Debbie?" Debbie accepts. Again she is being unusually congenial.

The bright neon lights of Tooshies bar, down on the next block, inspire me on to my feet.

"Would a bottle of Tequila go amiss on such a beautiful evening?"

"Certainly not John. I'll polish the shot glasses." The talk of shot glasses brings back thoughts of Angel. I hurry off in the direction of Tooshies.

"Tell me this Rick? When you were over the border did you carry anything? You know, guns? Whatever? They say those Mex cops are a tough bunch."

"You have to be jokin' bro'. We used to shoot the shit out of 'em when they got on our tail. Yes sir! Me and Mo, we'd fire like crazy sonofabitches. That was the easy bit. Give them there Mexs a magazine an' they backed right off." Rick laughs; he is enjoying his story-telling.

"The problems began this side o' the border, ridin' high on grass an' beer the State cops chase us clear out of gas." His laughter is softer now, shaking his head he clears his throat.

The Tequila snaps at my throat, salt adds to its bitter sting. The Zippo snaps at the roll ups and into the warm night we shoot the bull.

"Course, Jimmy got tagged M.I.A. I reckon Jimmy got so fucked up with all that was goin' down, he just turned plain native and is still living in some kampong on the Cambodian border".

"You reckon?"

"I know so. All this M.I.A is a load of crock. All them boys is now integrated into their new lives, wives and kids. They been there that long now, they have said goodnight to Uncle Sam."

Small embers from the make-shift barbecue warm Ben.

"You've been out that way, ain't you John?"

"Yeah, Borneo back in sixty-three. You boys was just taking off then." Debbie raises her eyebrows, sixty-three to her was a life time ago.

"Wuz dope the thing, I mean . . ." says Rick.

"No, I never seen it, never mind used it."

"Ain't that something."

"Use my bed tonight folks, I'll settle in the back of the pick-up with Ben. Just look at those stars Debbie. Do they have stars like these in New Mexico?"

It is a beautiful evening. The stars sparkle against the black velvet sky, begging you to reach up and steal them. The fire throws shadows over the palm trees and the giant Saguaro cactus. A man could find romance on a night like this. A scene set for lovers?

"Let's turn in Debbie." Rick has turned in some minutes ago. He is out of hearing range.

"Be careful John, I don't like that fucker. *Numero uno*."

"He's OK." Strange, she has hardly spoken a word all night.

"I am tired. Yes, let's go to bed."

Before I open my eyes, I know it's breakfast. The smell of bacon drifts through the cracks in the block work.

"You shouldn't do this Ricky . . ."

"You paid the tab last night man. What plans you got for today?"

"Dunno, lay back I suppose."

"Well I'm goin' to the flea market, I got me three boxes of goddamn Zippos to sell."

"What's the deal?"

"Seven apiece."

"I'm your first customer Rick, got change for ten?"

"Take this in to Debbie. Why don't you come on down later? All the old boys will be there, same old bunch as last year. Frank'll be there too. Remember Frank?"

"Maybe. Do me a favour Rick, don't let on I'm back in town. Right?"

"You get yourself over man! Drink a little beer and shoot the bull. Whatever, I'll catch you later."

He slams the cab door behind him. Ben instinctively leaps on to the tailboard and the truck rattles out of the compound.

Debbie grunts at the bacon sandwich so I eat it myself.

"I don't like it here John." She has the covers pulled tight up around her shoulders.

"Like I said, it's only days. We gotta hold up a while."

"It's a fucking joke. All that money and we are living in a place fit for pigs only."

"Rick's got enough problems of . . ."

"Rick fucking this! Rick fucking that! You got to wise up John. I hear you talking last night. You are losing it, do you know that? How do you know that now, at this very minute, he is not calling the police?"

"I don't think . . ."

"Think! You start to think, would it not help his situation with the parole board? Big with the fists and small with the brain."

Well Debbie, the quietness last night must have been the thinking you was doing. The thing is, she has a point, but even this I may work to my advantage.

"Get dressed Deb, we are on our way."

"You serious?"

"Serious. On the way out I have to call at the flea market. You stay in the car."

"Why?"

"No fuckin' questions Debbie, stay in the car."

This is some sized flea-market, huge ain't

the word, by far the biggest I've seen. Twenty feet separate line after line of posts, each one distributing electricity to the hundreds of trucks and cars lining the lot. Traders' rigs tie up here Friday through Sunday. Three good size canteens cater to the large crowds and there is a carnival atmosphere amongst traders and punters alike.

"Hey Frankie, here's your buddy from the old country."

"Checkin' out the territories again John? It's sure good to see you."

Nothing much has changed on the flea market circuit. The market is bigger but the faces are still the same. The climate attracts lots of these flea marketeers. Women and kids crammed into old cars, sleeping rough and hustling, but escaping the winters of the North and Mid-West.

"How ya doin' with the lighters Rick? Moving 'em?"

"Done me a box already man. Then the price is right. Yo bro!"

"Ribeye tonight eh? No beer for me thanks, I got some shopping to do."

I know Frankie's face from the Cerrillos market and we met up again last year in the company of Rick. He is a dealer if ever I saw one, sharp-eyed and dollar-wise. An old guy pulls up to the back of his rig. Inside the long beaten car sits a young kid, a trial bike half hangs out of the opened car trunk. The old-timer makes over to Frank. I gotta listen!

"Any of you boys interested in buyin' that there machine?" He points in the bike's direction. Frank scratches his head and looks about, then at me.

"Do we need a machine John?" I shake and drop my head.

"Sorry old-timer, my partner says we have no need."

"I sure as hell need to get rid. That kid over there, my grandson, well, to tell the truth, he ain't a full bag a shoppin'. He's riding the fuckin' thing all over the lawns, fallin' off an' upsetting every bastard in the neighbourhood."

"What you lookin' fer feller?" asks Frank. Now Granddad is scratching his head.

Frank inspects the bike. Grunts and low whistles have Granddad scratching his bollocks and fingering his arse. The kid looks on. He don't look a full bag of anything.

"Four hundred, and not a nickel less. It's only . . ."

"It ain't worth diddly, but I could deal. Wait a minute." Frank tracks off to his trailer, inside a scuffle ensues. He is back on to the baked earth with a sausage dog in tow, dragging it with a length of old rope.

Tell you what I'll do guy: this here dog for the bike. What do you say?" Indignant, the old man jumps on the spot, his bright red face ready to burst.

"Hey! Touch me, is this for fuckin' real. Am I dreamin'?" The old man is going bananas.

"Tell him the story John. How much did I git for each pup back in Santa Fe. No! I'll tell you. Fifty bucks a piece, yes sir. Now that ain't chicken shit."

The kid is in on the act, kneeling, stroking and patting Archie. Frank is moving in circles. What he doesn't know about bikes and sausage dogs ain't worth knowing. Slowly the old-timer gets sucked in.

"You have paperwork for the dog I take it?"

"Like I says, I bought this here Archie from a dude kennel back in west Texas. Tell him John. I think this ol' timer's a thinking I'm pulling 'is chain."

"Yeah, I can vouch for that." Frank found the dog on a slack Saturday. The dog was lost and looking for a home. He found Frank, and Frank seen an easy buck.

The old boy scratches about his person; the kid thinks it's Christmas and very soon I see it's gonna be game, set and match . . . to Frank.

"Just leave your address an' I'll mail the paperwork on once I gets back to Texas."

Before too long the pair are trailing dust, with two bowls thrown in because a deal's a deal. Frank rubs over the bike with an old shirt while his face reads (and I'm sure Frank believes) that he has come out of the deal evens. Frank's a diamond.

"So where you shoppin' John?"

"I'm goin' to move on Rick. South to Nogales, cross the border and rest up among the natives awhile."

"Be careful on the border brother, a man can get into plenty of trouble in them parts."

I see Ricky's mind turning over. Bastard, I have your card marked, but if the role's were reversed? I say my farewell and move slowly back to the Buick. Leaving Frank cosy on his deal and Rick with a head full of thoughts.

"Shoot some of the bastards for me." Shouts Rick. I don't look back.

I feel the heat from the Buick's running engine. Debbie looks over to me with those 'I told you so' eyes.

"I tell you something. You sure have some weird friends."

Debbie fires the engine and flips the AC.

"Where to Johnny?"

"Phoenix. Take High Ten for Casa Grande. Take it easy Deb, we don't want no law pulling us over."

"Sure dad!"

"Bollocks! Let's get off this lot."

"We need anything in Phoenix?"

"A launderette is what we need, before we hit Phoenix."

We pass plenty of launderettes scooting through Tucson's west side. I would like to stop but we have to distance ourselves from Rodeo Road so it's the middle lane on to Highway Ten. Will Rick make the call? I cannot take that chance. I'm fifty-fifty; Debbie's almost certain. As the mileometer ticks through its cycle, my shoulders loose their tenseness, so maybe she was right all along. After all, he's got nothing to lose and all to gain.

"There! Make for Casa Grande, we can rest up and do the wash. You OK Deb?"

"Aw, just thinking. When are we going to

make the ocean? Are we gonna be spinning wheels all over the south west or what?"

Spinning wheels is the last thing I have in mind. I had hoped we could have holed up at Rick's place a week or so. On hindsight, it was a stupid idea. Rick with his parole board problems. Frank and all the faces who know me from the last time I came this way. Then there was that story of us heading south into Nogales and old Mexico. Would the Feds swallow that? Would they fuck as like. Their records would show I'm carrying an out of date passport and the temporary green card ain't worth a wank. They know I'll stay this side.

They know there would be no problem going over the border, getting back though could be a little tricky. How long could I last amongst those bean brains? Not long and if there was an ID check on the US side, it's wham bam, straight into the slammer and, at best, shipped back to the country of pot holes and small meat pies. No, I don't even believe it; they won't believe it; nobody's gonna believe it. Staying this side at least I understand the language, even if sometimes nobody readily understands me.

"The air isn't workin' too good John." I shouldn't think so. As with her constant fiddling of the radio – she has tuned every station east of Moscow – the air switch has taken equal stick. If it turns, flicks, pulls out or pushes in, Debbie will mess with it.

"That's one thing I don't have a clue about."
She turns her head in surprise.

"You don't have air back home? You have refrigeration right?"

"Course we have. Just we don't have the climate. It's always pissin' down."

"Pissin' down?" She likes this description and laughs.

"Pull over! The garage right there. We might as well get it sorted. We sure as hell are goin' to need it."

"You sure about this?"

We bounce along rough ground and settle just short of two gas pumps. Behind the pumps sits a timber clapboard building. Held together with six inch nails and held down with tarpaulin and truck tyres. On first sight, this must combine office, canteen and card room for the half dozen or so hombres who lounge the porch. Some wear baseball caps but most wear weather-battered Stetsons, slung low to keep the sun from their faces. A lean-to has been tagged on to the office and acts as the garage. There is no mechanical equipment on show but these boys will surely have knowledge about air conditioning. Won't they?

This place is stuck in the middle of nowhere. The original proprietor obviously didn't have thoughts on making his millions. The dust settles and no one moves a muscle. It could be the shock of seeing someone.

"Stay in the car Deb."

"How ya doin' fellas? I got a problem here. Where do I find the mechanic?" Still no movement, but hats are tipped back and black beady eyes look me over. One pulls the ring on a beer; another taps a soft pack and draws a Lucky; another wipes sweat from his brow; and all the time their wind-creased faces stare, with eyes narrowed and jaws set firm. They shift on to Debbie, who is now at my shoulder.

They are all Hispanic and all middle-aged bar one, an old guy who's sat nearest to the doorway. He's slow on his feet, but he makes an effort and pushes open the fly screen and points inside. The office is cooled by an electric table fan. The only other item powered by the twentieth century is a large rounded refrigerator, full of beer no doubt. Two people sit behind an oak desk, their weight carried on sturdy Captain chairs. He is a tough looking leather-faced sonofabitch. She is a twenty something señora, dark hair and skin and showing signs of wear. A black cheroot glows as the fan moves by.

"Si?"

His voice is softer than his appearance. She looks on with interest. I now wish I had not come this far. Just turned at the pumps and found a garage in Casa Grande that was close to civilisation and where my English would be understood.

"I got trouble with the air conditioning.

Hang on! You tell him Deb." My speech is slow and clear. I would sooner have dealt with it myself, but Debbie knows the lingo. The cheroot is stubbed and I feel the best I'm gonna get out of this, is ripped off.

"No worry, no worry. I understand your English and your problem." Orders are barked and movement from the porch's rickety floor vibrates beneath my feet. His girl has lost all interest and manicures her finger nails. His attention now centres on Debbie.

"*Prep junto con?*" His voice has softened once more. Eyes flash between us.

"Yes." That's it Debbie. Keep it English.

"*Amigo*, eh, you friend. No?"

"Yes." The rest I don't understand. They gabble on for what seems a minute or so and must sense my impatience. Some of the lingo I get, words pertaining to foreigner, rich or poor, beautiful and such.

Lines form on his forehead. He is puzzled by this match. More hurried talk follows.

"What's going on Debbie?"

"He wants to know why I am with you."

"Tell him to mind his business and ask him what's with the air conditioning."

He understands my words well enough but instead of directing his talk my way, he rattles off at Debbie again. She is now firing back with short sharp bursts. Her anger is beginning to show.

"He still wants to know . . ."

"Señor, I have a problem with the car, no? It seems you have a problem with me, if that is so, please talk to me and not the lady." His eyes dart from me to his moll. She stands, opens the fridge and snaps the cap off a diet Pepsi. Her body language is signalling uninvolvement. Standing back, she sucks on the bottle.

"No problemo!" He says, taking the remains of the Pepsi from the girl.

He exits the office in silence. Debbie moves slowly alongside, her arm wraps my waist.

She whispers, "Where did you leave the money? Is it safe? Have you the gun? Be careful Johnny."

"The money is locked in the trunk. The piece in the glove compartment. Don't worry, we'll be out of here in no time." The owner appears back in the doorway.

"Por favor! The keys. Muchas gracias." He makes way as we push past him. The hood is raised and two heads are nodding away besides the engine, one making low whistling noises. The rest of the crew are still sat on the porch, their hats pushed right back, taking note of all that is happening. They obviously heard our conversation in the office.

The hood is dropped and the two mechanics stand back, making room for the boss man. Brooom! The Buick comes to life.

"OK, OK my friend, everything is fixed now. Servico, it's good, you see?" His mechanics have moved alongside him. I have the feeling it's time to go.

"What's the bill?"

"Veinte, veinte." The palm of his hand shows four times. "Cheap eh? Come again my friend and bring the señorita also. We make you welcome." Rapid Spanish shoots between the men. They laugh as Debbie leans across me, her face now close to the open window.

"Tell him, go fuck himself." Shout it out Deb! The Mex's head lowers to view Debbie. I'm peeling off a twenty. He's laying Spanish into her. Anything else you need to say? The gear slides into drive while the twenty is screwed tight and flicked at him. Surprise as the note hits his chest then falls to earth. Anger shows on his face. His men wait for orders.

"Yeah motherfucker . . ." I call. The foot brake is released and looking back I see dust settling on leaping figures, arms raised, fists shaking after us.

"Are you happy now Debbie?"

"I'm happy."

Casa Grande is home to ten and a half thousand people, the roadside sign tells me so. During the drive off the highway I have seen little cattle and no industry. Moving closer I see a tired-looking town, so where do people work? How do they make the rent? I can only guess they take in each other's laundry, and if that's the case, I'm in luck. Into town, we cut right and cruise Main Street, Debbie on the look out for that launderette.

"Here! No! There! The next block, gee, you missed it." I did see it but I had a low rider up my arse and couldn't make the switch.

"Aw John! You never listen to a word I say. You're gonna have to swing right and come around the block."

I'm listening, like I'm always listening. Women eh? They have all the pussy, half the money and still they have it they are always getting the raw deal.

"Good job you have me along Johnny. Where would you be?" Some place else, doing a wash for one and not getting myself almost killed for air conditioning.

"That was something else back there, wasn't it? Scary, if you ask me."

"So, what was the beef? What was being said? What were they up to?"

"Like you would not believe. They wanted me John. If I had been on my own, hey; I wouldn't pull into a place like that – it's too dangerous. Another thing, they don't like Anglos fuckin' their best pussy. They like to keep it all to themselves."

"Best pussy eh? They know something I don't then! Anyway, tell me what was said?"

"He said you are an ugly old man, skinny and English to boot. What the hell do you think he said?"

"What do I think? I think I should have left you back there. That's what I think."

I miss my turn, shoot the lights and, you wouldn't believe it, the AC packs in again!

Watching the wash. The monotony is broken when a thin Mex arrives with a wagon load of kids. They are on top of machines, under machines and inside them. They are driving the wash assistant wild and I have to walk out front to snatch a cigarette. There are six of them and they came in like it's Disney Land. Even Debbie has had enough and joins me on the sidewalk.

"Are you going to feed me today honey?" Honey is not a word she uses often. There must be a catch!

"What's with the 'honey', honey?"

"Don't you think I need some more tennis shoes? Look at these would you. Do you feel ashamed when you walk with me?"

"If you need a pair, just ask. There's no need to make a three act play out of it."

"They sell LA Gear over the street. I have always wanted a pair." At least I'll have time on my own to think.

"There is loose change in the glove compartment. Take what you need, OK?"

"OK." She skips across to the car. There is

fuck all wrong with the ones she's got. Still, if it keeps her happy.

That's it Debbie, lock the car and give me back the keys. I don't want you and the new LA Gear taking off some place. Looking back into the launderette, I see the kids' old man doing his nut. How long is this wash going to take? I would have left it with the assistant, but you can't trust any bastard. So, marking time, I reflect on another near miss, such as the one back at the garage. This is bandit country, no mistake, and although Debbie likes to think the gun is part of my macho make up, one would be a fool to travel these parts without one.

Last year, taking the high road out of El Paso and ten miles south of the New Mexico State line, I pull into a rest area. I had spent the previous night stretched on the Chevy's bench seat. Even with the help of a six-pack, it was a bummer of a night, a couple of hours sleep was all. Needing somewhere to wash down and tip the empties, the rest area looked the place to be. Smack bang in front of the rest rooms is parked a long haulage truck, its red and chrome glistening in the sunshine. Pulling in opposite I note the driver, busy writing in his cab, pad resting on the steering wheel.

The only other vehicle is an old beaten Ford Galaxy 500. It's not only the condition of the car that stands out, it's the paint job, black. Now that's a strange colour to be driving in the desert heat, and that's the reason I remember the make and model. In the passenger seat sits a heavy looking Mex, clocking my plate. They are both the real thing, out of old Mexico.

He throws me a shifty eye and a shitty grin exposing bad teeth. I glance up at the trucker, he shoots me a quick one then returns to his writing. Well, I'm here, in need of that wash down and breaking my neck for a piss. Greaser is sat in the passenger seat so it's obvious his oppo is somewhere in the rest room. I should have been thinking, wait it out, they are bound to take off shortly, but my cheeks are pinching shit and times running out!

Inside, his friend is taking a leak, his belly strokes the urinal as he spends forever shaking his dick. I'm watching him through the mirror and I see he's watching me. Warm water splashes on to my face. He's still shaking. Where I come from, anything over ten shakes is classed as a wank. I dare not go for a crap because I'd leave myself open to ambush, cornered with my pants down, so to speak.

Splashing more water, I watch him walk behind me, then, as he nears the exit, he breaks out into a trot. Ha! The bastard's gone for his mate. Concealed in a towel sits a primed .38, the towel is swiftly picked up and I move to the washbasin furthest away from the door. My right hand rests inside the towel, the .38 still hidden away in case some innocent vacationer comes breezing in. Minutes pass with no sign of a return visit, so, gathering up towel and toothbrush I venture out.

The Ford has gone, but not the trailer. The driver is standing out front his open cab door. Arms folded, his eyes never leave me as I break ground for the Chevy. Once I open my cab door, he lifts his thumb in the air then swings up into his seat. What's he telling me? You're a stupid sad ass is what he's telling me. I read the picture; the Mex comes flying out, signals his opposite number, spots the trucker. Wait a second, those arms are folded, is he concealing a weapon? The trucker stands his ground. They go to ground and I got lucky. Thanks a lot pal.

Through the glass and between the kids, I see the machine has stopped. Debbie returns, walking on air and proud of her new footwear.

"LA Gear John! I've always wanted LA Gear."

"They look good on you. You bought the socks to match, eh?"

"Yes."

"You're lookin' good. Listen Deb I still have to dry this lot; why don't you walk across the street and order food. That's it, the small deal on the corner."

"Sure. You have anything in mind? Or do you want me to order the same as me?" Her hand rubs small circles on her stomach.

"And no chilli, red or green, it don't matter. I've been shitting through the eye of a needle all morning. Do your best eh, no chilli." She turns and waits for traffic to clear.

"Debbie! Make it a ribeye, mushrooms if they have them."

"Sure they'll have them, silly Englishman."

Debbie leaves me to the drying, and my thoughts. We ain't going to make the ocean. Where would we go? Some crowded city like Los Angeles? It couldn't be anywhere else, could it Debbie? "I got the pumps" and all that shit! Like a fish out of water, confused and frustrated, she wouldn't last two minutes, and neither would I. No Deb, between here and the ocean is where we'll be.

Mama Casa's is small. Bums on seats ain't the priority as there are only five tables, linen-covered. Afternoon tea and scones are being taken by a middle-aged couple. It is all very civilised, a far cry from the fast food joints we seem to visit every day. The only other occupied table is ours.

"Would you believe it Debbie. That air conditioning has packed in." I didn't mention it earlier. With LA Gear her uppermost priority, would it have registered?

"No shit!" Go back an' ask for the twenty back."

"Really!"

Debbie is knifing through a steak, so I guess she is having a troubled bowel.

"Steak okay John?"

"Great. What happened to the mushrooms?"

"Forgot. Cannot be thinking of everything. Where are we staying tonight? Are we going to get the air fixed?"

"We'll keep the windows open. Tonight? I dunno, but we got to make it through Phoenix at least."

"Make it some place nice eh? With a pool, ice machine and . . ."

"You brought a costume?!"

"I bought a costume, you know, when I bought the LAs. Is there something wrong?"

"No, but take it easy. It's gotta last you know."

"Do you love me John?" Do I love her? Now there's a question. This isn't Debbie. This isn't a word that trips off her tongue lightly and I'm not too sure I like it and I'm certainly not prepared. Could I love this child-like creature? Another time, another place maybe. Not now. I tire of her company easily, her deviousness unsettles me – I should talk. Hump an' dump 'em, no promises and no commitment. Who am I trying to kid? Truth is, the more she is around me, the closer I'm getting.

"I love you best I can. Have I ever let you down? Listen to me, and listen good. When the time comes for good-byes, you'll be the one saying them."

"Love me the best you can? Is that it? What's that add up to?"

"Hey! Who married you back there in Vegas? Who bought you the car? What more do I have to do?" My arms fling open in false despair. Debbie spikes the remains of her steak and waves it in my face.

"You married me for the green card. Yes you did! And you bought that shit car in my name so it could not be traced back to you. Mamma! You must think I'm fucking stupid and you're so, so clever. Oh yeah. Oh fuckin' yeah! That easy smile, that easy way you have. The way you play with people, just you remember. What goes around, comes around."

"You know you mean a lot to me. Come on now Debbie, we wouldn't be on the road together otherwise. Would we?"

"I suppose not. Just promise me . . ."

"Everything will be just fine, you'll see."

BE A GOOD BOY JOHNNY 10

Hugging the south side of Phoenix, we skirt Sky Harbor International Airport. Big birds line and taxi the runway. There must be room in one of them for Debbie. She looks across and reads my thoughts.

"Don't even think about it John." I roll my shoulders and concentrate on the oncoming road signs. Where's it going to be?

Up to now I have had a good start on whoever has that hard-on for me. They are out there. Soon, every cop car that comes close, every guy that looks at me twice will have me thinking, this is it, the final knock down, the final count out. You can run but you can't hide. With Debbie by my side I can't shoot it out, or run that extra mile against the law.

Already I'm eye-balling the rear view mirror like they teach you when you're seventeen, then you forget when you're eighteen. Wait on! Did I see that Dodge back at the last pumps? That black four by four? Hasn't it passed four times in the past mile or so? That Volkswagen camper looks . . . What am I thinking? Only born again hippies drive those rattlers.

"Hey Johnny! Those old eyes, they don't read the signs no more. You're headin' through for Sun City." Sure thing Debbie. Shit! We have to get off the main trunk road. The call is out and sooner or later, at a gas pump or road diner, an agent or whoever is going to pick up on my accent or plate number.

"Where we goin'?" We're riding to nowhere baby, that's where. Eighty seven grand, the big sting, now burning a hole in me. Just had to do it, there it was. Now, like warm milk, it's turning sour. I'm looking at ten to fifteen years, surrounded in the State Pen by buck nigger shirt-lifters and spending long days and longer nights with my back to the wall.

"What on earth are you playing at Johnny?"

"Shut the fuck up! Any more Debbie, an' I swear I'll turn about an' drop you back at the airport."

"Like fuck you will."

What's the worst possible scenario? The dope heads dropping by. It's lights out. I'd be brown bread, and so would Debbie. She don't see the big picture. This ain't Hollywood and this ain't going to end with a dramatic car chase on the Grand Canyon rim. No sir, whatever you have tucked away in that tiny head of yours, it's gonna get drilled and spilled and hey, you might even make a mention on radio AM KTAR 620 or the back pages of the local rag. Debbie's never gonna see the picture. She's riding to the great sugar candy mountain. Find it sweet baby, find it sweet.

Clear of Phoenix and cruising directions reading Sun City, I wipe over the ten-buck shades. Looking east and west, I can see forever through the clean air. I barely notice the naked mountains and prickly desert floor. Where we goin'? It's going to come to me soon. Come on John, you've been down this road before. The rules, remember? The rules change, but the game is always the same.

"Sun City heh John. Ain't that where the old go to die?"

"It's where the middle-classes go to die, that's where."

Sun City spreads its condos and golf courses. This huge complex houses upwards of sixty thousand people. The aged, with property to sell and fat pensions to draw, settle here to play their ultimate hole.

"Such a smart ass. You're gonna be tellin' me next, you've travelled this very road."

"No Debbie, I've never been this way before. Did you know a person has to be at least fifty-five before they can buy a home in Sun City?"

"Ain't that something. Just swing on in an' stick that old grey head of yours out of the cab an' perhaps they'll fix you up."

"Very funny. You're gonna crack me up. I spent some time in Phoenix though."

"An' I never crossed my own State line 'til this very week. Ain't that something?"

"That's something alright."

"What was you doing in Phoenix then?"

It's not Debbie's nature to ask about the past. With her, it's always the future. Show me a woman that's never asked if you're married, been married or had kids and I'll give you the cash that's stashed under the driver's seat. Debbie's a first. I hunch my shoulders and steady the gas pedal.

"Aw Johnny, come on. Tell me?" She has noted my impatience and concentration over the past miles. I can only guess it's her way of opening me up and steadying me down.

"It was a kinda vacation. The couple I came to see were old, just like them behind the high-tech surveillance over there. Have you ever heard of Scotsdale?"

"Yeah, ain't that where the rich live?"

"That's right, but that don't mean a thing though. These are good people."

"Good people shit! Old folks eh! You must have had a ball is all I can say." Is it any use carrying on? Where Debbie comes from, Anglo rich comes at the expense of Hispanic poor. Back to your magazine Debbie. Let me wind down the window some and let more air inside this bus.

*   *   *

The last time I was in Phoenix the city was in darkness and in the grip of a raging monsoon. Rain lashed the windshield wipers to a standstill while palm-tops swayed overhead and tried to break free from their trunks. Lost and in need of company, I ride a ramp and buy coffee and use the change to make a call. I'm a hour adrift but Harry says no problem. I'm but five blocks away and he'll be waiting on the corner of Eleventh at nine o'clock.

I'd gunned down from Flagstaff with some trepidation. How was I going to fit with this couple? One week is a long time to be making jigsaws. Still, I can always make an excuse to be someplace and move along.

Harry's right on the corner as I slide to a halt. T-shirt and lightweight slacks rolled to his knees. He springs into the cab like a man half his seventy years.

"Harry?"

"Yeah, you sure picked your night. Nice to meet with you John. That's it, sharp right. Straight on now."

"Sorry I'm late. Got me lost, rain an' all."

"Don't worry. We don't go to bed early these days. Do you like to drink John?" Do I say yes? Then he thinks I'm a drunken bum. Do I say no and keep everybody happy?

"Yes."

"Good. You an' me are going to do some serious drinking. You up to that?"

"I'll do my best Harry."

What a week! Harry must have an account down at the corner liquor store. Every evening at six o'clock prompt, he tops off a fresh pint of Jack. He takes ice now he tells me, but the old buzzard can neck it down. By Wednesday I'm struggling like a novice, one pint behind. It's the stories that keep me awake. Thing is, Harry retired out off the State Attorney's Office. He talks all night long about this and that, East coast mobsters who now live on Tucson's south side. Vast tracks of land were bought to house their favoured and fortunate. Their names don't mean a thing to me, but Harry's interesting all the same.

Daytime sees Harry and his red Mustang gone. Yeah, seventy and a Mustang reads seventy and a mistress to me! I shake myself into life and settle back with Harry's old lady. Maggie is younger than Harry, by several years I guess, but she has Alzheimer's disease which gives her a child-like appearance and child-like mannerisms. Harry still keeps her car in the garage, but hides the keys. All morning she spends looking for them or following me around the home, sits when I sit and repeatedly asks my name and where I come from.

I'm a ready-made sitter for Harry. Maggie and I sit by the half-filled swimming pool out back. Shaded by the tall palm trees, we plop small stones at the leaves and bugs that cover the pools surface. Harry arrives back, a meal is thrown together and at six we start another drinking session.

This one night, Thursday I think it was, Harry asks a favour. Would I walk Maggie down to the hair salon, next door to the liquor store. Every Thursday she gets it fixed. Fine by me. We walk in the warmth of early evening, a pleasant breeze and the moon is full and high. It was kinda strange, holding on to her like that. I dare not let her go. Hey! Watch the traffic. She sits under the dryer while I sit out front on the kerb, smoking and day dreaming.

One hour later, Maggie is escorted out and joins me on the kerb. We are sat way back off the main drag on a small road that fronts the row of shops. She is enjoying this, I can tell. Her eyes are bright and her movements jerky. She points to the sky. Small aircraft blip their tail lights. All this time I'm talking nonsense: trees, stars, planes, anything to keep her attention.

"See those? I used to fly them." She slaps her legs. I'm caught off balance.

"You did?" We are not too far from the airport. The sky seems to be full of those tiny flashing lights.

"Sure, when I was twenty." I smile and squeeze her hand.

"You did? You remember that?"

That's what I remember most. That lovely old lady, her brain bombed out now, but the shine

BE A
GOOD BOY
JOHNNY

that came over her face that night will stay with me a long time. Last I heard, Harry had her moved into a nursing home. Harry told me next day she did fly solo. He told me in a matter of fact way but I bet she was some gal when she was twenty.

"Did you know Elvis was seen in a New York diner? Only last week." It's Debbie. Welcome back to the real world!

"What are you readin' now? The funny papers?" Debbie tosses the pages over her shoulder; they split and scatter along the back seat.

"All the time you have to pull me down. What is it with you? Just once . . ."

"You believe that shit Debbie? Give me a break! We're close on Wickenburg. We'll stop there and stretch our legs. What ya say?"

"I ain't saying nothin' no more." Yeah, yeah.

Across a narrow bridge we enter Wickenburg. I raise the pedal and ride the speedo on the ten. A small neat town lays before us and I reckon we'll be through and out the other side if the gear box makes third. Stopping on Valentine Street I let Debbie off outside Anita's Cocina.

"Order what you want Deb. I'll park up and catch you in ten or fifteen minutes."

"Give me a twenty John. Why don't you park here? You're comin' back. Right?"

"I ain't leaving it in the open. Here, hold my passport. You don't trust me none, do ya?" She would trust me even less if she knew the passport was out of date.

"As far as I could fuckin' throw you. Does that answer your question?"

"Ten minutes."

I lock up and shake my legs. I'm going to walk the aches away so I head up past the library. Wouldn't I like to look inside and browse through the books. Another time. I'm looking at a tidy little town, clean sidewalks and brightly-painted wooden buildings. Another thing I see is, everyone appears to be Anglo, the town's name tells me it's founder was German and sometimes they stay that way, isolated and suspicious to outsiders.

A couple of old-timers sit beneath a turn of the century locomotive. It's a statue to some time or another and the couple look like they rode with her. I ask them if there are any trailer parks close by and after deliberation I'm told to drive north aways and look out for a sign post. There's more, but that's the closest. The old boys talk the fights. Zale, Ray Robinson, Cerdan, Turpin, Graziano, LaMotta and more. All tough middleweights from the forties and fifties. I know the fight game so I perch myself on to the end of the bench and listen in.

I sit to the right of them, always the right these days, hiding the scar. It puts people on the wrong track. At least I think it does. They know their boxing and I think of cutting in on the action.

I leave it and torch a cigarette, kick my desert boots a few feet away then massage the stiffness and heat away from my toes. The right side eh? Always the right. There are old habits that are routine now, like walking into the john. Always use the far right urinal, then if trouble comes along at least you can turn quickly, get balanced and throw the right from the shoulder. How many men do this as a matter of routine? Not many, but then these routines never got me to the top of any class when I was a kid.

Now the scar. That's the main reason I'm bumming around Uncle Sam. Okay, in some style at the moment, but for how long? The scar came one rainy November night back home. Home being wherever I happened to be at any one time. This time it was in the north-west of England. There is a boozer ahead, just over the railway bridge. I'm not fifty yards away. Like I said, it's raining cats and dogs. My hands are dug deep into my pockets, pulling the crombie out of shape.

The collar is up and my hands are the only dry thing between here and the pub. The Oxfords beat a more than steady pace. I'm late on account of missing my bus and the lads have a taxi booked for eight-thirty. Anyway, just over the bridge I see three figures standing there. On a night like this? They stand like kids. The nearer I get, I see they are kids. I don't give it much thought, but anyone with half a brain wouldn't be standing out in this lot.

They close down the pavement. Cheeky bastards!
I brace my shoulders to push them over.

Wooosh! I don't see the steel, I don't feel the pain, but all of a sudden the side of my face warms up and that ain't rainwater running on to my collar. There were warning signs. I had freed my hands, but these were kids after all. Kids or no kids, the damage is done. Two scarper, but the one that did the damage, lucky for me, unlucky for him, slips on the wet gutter cobble stones.

I'm on him faster than a fly on shit. Where's the blade? I see it, he's dropped it trying to break his fall. My weight pins him to the cobbles, his young face looks up at me, a pleading I-didn't-mean-to-do-it mister look. Pain is already etched in his face, he knows he's gonna get it, but he don't know how. My right hand grips the Stanley. I feel the need to open his face, take an eye, slash the bastard to shreds.

This kid cannot be more than seventeen. What's it about? A dog barks, a front gate opens, aint got time to find the reasons. Stab, thud, thud, the blade crashes down into his thigh. He's screaming like a stuck pig and before long we have a crowd around us. Nobody needs to pull me away, I stand at my own speed. I didn't make the taxi and to top it all, I have to share an ambulance with the twat. On the run to the hospital, he's getting the sympathy and I'm getting looks that would kill from the crew. I'm not reading this right, am I?

Under the interior lighting of the ambulance, I clock his face for future reference. It ain't ending here pal!

It did end there. Turns out the kid was fifteen years of age. Just fifteen. I'm advised that I could be looking at a stretch for sticking a minor, so fuck them. I'll take my chances in the wild woolly west with all those Injuns. Anyway, what with the weather and a warrant out for my arrest, it was time to blow.

Charles, Marciano, Jersey Joe, Louis and that English bum Cockell. The last named, lightly thrown in my direction. They have reached the heavies and my watch tells me it's time for me to find Debbie.

"Where the fuck have you been?" She's standing outside the restaurant, hands on hips and turning heads.

"Have you eaten?"

"No! I've been worried to death on where you might be at. Tell me?"

"Talkin' with some old guys down by the parking lot. Talkin' an' smokin' is all."

"You and old guys! I'm getting worried about you."

"Let's go back inside then?"

"Ain't hungry no more." She don't have the twenty, so I take it she's left it on the table.

Who cares? I would sooner be getting my balls chewed off out here than in there.

"Do you want to look around or head for the car?" I say looking up and down the sidewalk.

"Look at what? I seen enough of this piss 'ole already an' it's cost me twenty. Okay, okay, maybe stop by and buy a box of cold Pepsi. If we had a cooler box, we could buy ice. We need a cool box John. Come on, get with it man!"

"Let's go an' find a box then."

We move north. Debbie's sucking on a Pepsi and I'm looking hard for the Western Days Trailer Park. Half a mile of bumpy track later, we swing through an opening in the ranch fencing. There ain't but twenty trailers, dotted here and there. All are old, most have their lower skirting missing, exposing plumbing and waste pipes.

The shells of old pick-ups dot the perimeter, along with engine blocks and scrap of all kinds. Debbie has been quiet along the bumpy track. I see her brain turning over. This is not like Debbie!

"You know somebody on this site?"

"Nope."

"Well! What the fuck are we doin' here? You're not thinking on taking one of these old trailers, are you? Count me out! This is about as far as it gets from the ocean. Just tell me you're havin' a brainstorm or something. Well John?"

"We need some place to wind down, Debbie. Look, I know I'll have to put one month's rent down, but we won't be but ten days, two weeks at most, I promise."

"You're jokin'?"

"Yeah, yeah, I'm fuckin' joking. Listen to me, we got to stop runnin' and kick back a while. I'm goin' to run right back up my own arse, I swear."

"Kick back eh? What we gonna do?" My mind goes back to the library.

"I dunno, read. Hey! I'll buy a portable television . . ."

"Read! You have to be shittin' me. I came all this way to read? It's a fucking joke is what it is. You hearing me?"

"It's not what you think. We have to be careful, you know that. Be reasonable, that's all I ask."

"Reasonable! It's reasons I got. Where have the promises gone? The ocean? To be somewhere different for once in my life.

"We'll be there, trust me."

"Yeah, when I'm old an' grey like you! I've had it!"

"Well! We're bitchin' now ain't we?"

The talking stops as someone official from the trailer park moves alongside the car. A thick leather belt holds him together.

"You guys in need of help? Ain't got ourselves lost now, have we?"

"We've been lost for ever mister."

"You'll have to excuse the wife, I think the sun has finally got to her. Wouldn't happen to have a trailer for rent, would you?"

"Might have. Kill the engine an' I'll take a look back in the office."

The office bit don't cut mustard. It's his way of upping the ante.

"All those promises John. You never meant to keep any of 'em. It's no good piling on the bullshit; it's gettin' old is what it is."

"Hell! I shoulda dropped you back in El Paso. Moanin' an' groanin' is all I hear."

"What the . . ."

"Keep it down – he's on his way back."

He signals us to park up in front of his office. He ambles off and I follow. Debbie stays in the Buick; the ignition keys stay in my pocket.

"It's a single wide, an' to be honest we've had better. The owners have gone east 'til New Year. If you're plannin' on stayin' longer, another might come available before then. You plannin' on stayin' that long?" We are now standing in front of the red and cream painted single wide.

"Could be, but this would tide us over."

"You folks have work around here? I ain't being nosy you understand." He's worried about the rent payments.

"There's no problem with money, if that's your worry. What are you asking?"

"One sixty a month, but look inside an' see what y'all think."

I reckon the fat man is sub-letting this trailer, but do I care. A skinny teenage girl in white shorts and red boob tube steps down from the next trailer. The fat man's eyes follow mine as I follow her. There's a story somewhere. I see it written all over his sweaty face. The inside ain't bad. Four burner cooker and fridge. Easy chairs and double bed with linen. An old television sits in the corner, so that will save on the portable. All in all . . . I'm going to take it. I'll try and Jew him down.

"One sixty eh? That's the best you can do?"

"That's the bottom line fella. Take it or leave it, an' time I don't 'ave a lot of." Why? Where you going? Perhaps he's got something going with the jail bait that's now stood not ten feet from the door way. Shoeless and with that hungry look for cock, she pushes her damp hair to the side. The Buick is hidden from view, and it's just as well. Debbie would be out and this young one wouldn't stand a chance with the alley cat.

I give it another walk round. Checking the burners and flicking the switch on the refrigerator.

"The roof don't leak, does it?"

"Not to my knowledge." He's getting edgy, looking over his shoulder all the time, right out the doorway at the girl. Maybe I'm in the way and other things are on his mind right now.

"I'll take it. You'll want a month up front?"

"Yeah. A month'll settle it."

"Let me get the wife, she'll want to give it

the once over. Don't get me wrong on this pal, but I don't think that young girl is gonna help matters." He can take this any way he likes, I don't give a monkey's. I got enough problems of my own already. He gets the picture and reddens up. I've read this right. You dirty, lucky bastard!

Debbie don't brighten up none. In a way she's back in the *barrio*. These kind of people round her, it takes her back to where she came from. Me? I'm made up. This is about as safe a place as I could wish. It's gonna be a lucky man that even dreams about driving that bumpy track. This will do, but what about Debbie?

"I know you're tryin' your best Johnny, but it ain't good enough. I'm going to die in some shit-hole like this? It's the story of my life, goddamn it."

"Sit down luv. I'll tell you what I'll do."

"Give me a cigarette?"

"You don't smoke."

"Give me one all the same."

It sits between her lips. Funny thing, it sits the wrong way round, the filter reaching out.

"Seein' as we're in this shit together and knowing if I get hit . . ."

"Don't be talkin' like that."

"Like I'm saying. If it should happen, there ain't goin' to be nothing for you. So this is it. Look at me! The gun, I'm going to leave it in this drawer. The money I'm going to split down the middle. Half with me, the other half hidden in the car. You know where I hide it, so if anything comes down at least you got a shot. You have the car and thirty grand. You got this?"

She's got it alright. I don't see her rushing to unpack. Come on Debbie, this is it. I'm handing it to you on a plate. Her thoughts are racing.

"I'll get my cases." She walks slowly through the door. She's thinking on it. She turns and flicks the cigarette at me. There is no emotion, her eyes are dead. Those dancing eyes that greeted me on McCarren airport, they ain't there no more. Gone forever. One day, someone else will drown in them. Me? I'm history.

She takes forever bringing the cases in. I know she's left anything of value in the trunk. How are you going to say those good-byes Debbie? Funny thing is, I'm going to miss you. We're too much of a likeness. Whoever comes along next, I'm going to get the same old shit, but with you at least you was good to look at and dynamite between the sheets. Another thing, we travelled a road together. All that shit back in Santa Fe, it's like we're bonded, seen each other's grey areas, at least you mine.

"Lock the door John and take me to bed . . . I'm tired."

This is not the best of good-byes. I can't make it. Her flesh is soft and wet with sweat. She smells all woman, but it's no use, I'm in freefall.

I see Wayne, leeching a beer on the strength of another tall story. I see Angel sticking out her tits and me counting her money. I see Jeff telling me how I ain't going to make it out of the country. I see Greg and that other fuck-face in the bar that night. I see them all and none of it's too pretty. I'm sorry baby, catch me another time.

She falls asleep and I kind of catnap. An hour goes by then she wrestles herself to the toilet. I lay there and watch her through the open door, I'm sure she doesn't know I'm watching, and I'm sure it wouldn't make any difference anyway. Watching her wash and brush her teeth, unhurried, the way all women seem to do.

"We'll be wanting some supplies around here. What you say we ride back into town and load up?"

"Okay Debbie, let me sort that business with the money first."

She shrugs her shoulders and begins to pull the bedding together. Outside the park is alight, every trailer contributing some wattage to fend off the darkness. Barring the fat man and the girl, this is the first sign of life I have seen. Now there's the odd dog barking, low talk behind curtains and in the distance a coyote howl. The trunk light throws on to Debbie's clothing, most of it is still here. The cases she carried in must have been almost empty, so we're getting closer. On the car bench seat I count out the bills. Already they are folded

197

BE A
GOOD BOY
JOHNNY

into thousand dollar lots. I count to ten and push them under the bench. She was never going to get the thirty.

What would she do with all that money? Greg would get his teeth fixed and the rest would be pissed up the wall. No, with that and the car, I think you've done alright. You might even have loose change to buy that ring you're always bitchin' about. I shall not be hanging around here too long either. Once you are back in Santa Fe, the police are going to ask you all the right questions. And as sure as night follows day you are going to give them the right answers. In two days' time the Days Trailer Park will be swarming with cops.

We bounce down the track, one second the headlights peer into craters, next they are lighting up the sky.

"You hungry John?" These are her first words since getting aboard.

"I am. You want to stop some place before we shop?"

"That will be nice." Those words don't sit right.

"Wasn't there a McDonalds as we came into town? You know, down by that narrow bridge?"

"There is one there, you're right. We'll stop by, no problem." I look across, but I can't see her, just her outline, but her presence is stronger than ever.

The drive down to and through the town is

tense. I try opening up a conversation, but she ain't having any of it. Only a few vehicles dress the burger-lot so I park close up to the window.

"What do you want?"

"Anything, Big Mac, anything."

"Since when has anything been alright with you?"

"Since tonight, big shot!"

"Okay by me. I'll get you anything. You comin' inside?"

"No, I'll stay right here. Listen to the music an' take in the air."

I'm their only customer at the counter, so I reckon on fast service. This food I wouldn't feed a dog. To be honest I don't know the menu – I must be the only person in America – so the Big Macs look an easy option. As the order is being made up I turn and look at Debbie. Through the windshield I see her, drumming fingers on the dash. She's watching me. I point to the ketchup, she nods.

"An' two Cokes to go please." Come on Debbie, it ain't going to get better than this. Go! I look back through the window. A pick-up is drawing alongside Debbie. She's still looking at me, her right hand drops off the dash. The pick-up kills its engine; the Buick fires. Her face is dead-pan, her mouth forming silent words. "Be a good boy Johnny . . . Be a good boy . . . Be a good boy . . ."

She slowly reverses off the lot. It's like she

knows I ain't going to chase after her. Slowly out on to the highway and on to that narrow bridge. You'd better make a stop for gas soon! The Cokes get trashed in the waste bin. Outside I take a plastic seat and look down the bridge. It's dark and I don't see a thing. Eating into the burger I glance down at the Rolex. Fifteen to midnight. An old mangy dog turns the corner. Hey! Is that you chilli dog? Where you been? Come and join me, I got food for two. You have to be quick pal. In fifteen minutes a Greyhound is going to pull in at the terminal one block west and I'm jumping aboard for that ride to the ocean.

He takes a long hard look. I'm sure I see his mouth forming those words "Be a . . ."

Get outta here!